MAN INTO WOMAN

GILBERT OAKLEY

About the Author . . . .

GILBERT OAKLEY was born in Kent in 1916. His father was T. GILBERT OAKLEY, Member of the National Association for Mental Health, and Chief Consultant to the Pelman Institute up to his death in 1953.

GILBERT OAKLEY was educated at St. Cecelia's School and St. Aloysius College, Highgate, London. Also at Skerry's College and the Glasgow School of Art. He served in the Second World War from 1940 to 1946.

After the war, MR. OAKLEY became Editor of a national monthly Health Magazine. He has written 18 books since 1953 and is now a free–lance Editor and Author.

MAN INTO WOMAN

The amazing account of a male's change into female, with full psychological and medical Case History and Personal Analysis Questionnaire

By

GILBERT OAKLEY
D.Psy.

ILLUSTRATED

WALTON PRESS
LONDON

1ST IMPRESSION — FEB. 1964

Made & Printed by
THE WALTON PRESS
525/7 LIVERPOOL ROAD, LONDON, N.7

AUTHOR'S NOTE

A man born with a withered arm is greatly to be pitied. Life is made as easy as possible for him. If he is born without legs—the State is ready to help him. If he is born mentally deficient—he is well cared for.

If he develops some malignant disease as he passes from childhood to adulthood—hospitalisation is the answer. If he suddenly loses his reason due to a nervous breakdown or a serious accident —there are willing folk to make the remainder of his life bearable.

If a man is born with the body of a man—but with the mind of a woman—exactly how much sympathy and understanding does he receive? If, as he grows up, his body begins to change from male to female—how much kindness and solicitude does he get from friends, family, onlookers, the State, the Church, the medical profession?

Not so very much.

Because sex has reared one of its uglier heads.

The man has become an embarrassment. He is dubbed a ' queer '. A homosexual.

If the body-mind conflict gets too much for him and he appears in public in female dress—he is quickly hauled out of sight by the law. If he pursues his unasked-for obsession and annoys men or women—he may be certified.

If he is forced to go through life with his man-woman mind and body, he may commit suicide from frustration, repression and inhibition.

This book presents just this problem. The problem of the man born with too many female sex chromosomes in a male body. The man over whom nature could not make up her mind when the embryo child was still in the womb. The man who suffered from an imbalence of male and female content.

If a child in the foetus develops male characteristics that stop short of, say, the 30 mark—the balance of female sex factors will be 70. So he will be born 30 per cent. male and 70 per cent. female.

There is no such thing as a man or a woman with a perfect balance of sex hormones—or a man or a woman who is one hundred per cent. male or female. There is always that little difference on one side or the other. Rarely, also, is distribution of sexual chromosomes and hormones **perfectly equal.**

Nature sometimes plays a shabby trick.

A child is born with a man's body to all intents and purposes, but with a female mentality that, later in life, will predominate. or he is born with a plethora of female physical characteristics that, later in life, will begin to make themselves apparent.

So the time arrives when a terrible mental conflict begins in the mind of such a man—' Am I a male or a female ? '

And . . . in so many cases—the desire to be feminine is overwhelming.

Such a man develops, many times, at an early age—into a trans-sexual. A man who wants to transfer his sex. He pursues this fantasy either by cross-dressing in private, or he wants to have the operation of phallectomy performed on him for the complete and final removal of his male physical sexual characteristics.

This book is a plea for more understanding for a man in such a dire plight.

This book is founded on fact.

Its main character—Julian Griffiths—is the personification of many well-known transvestites and trans-sexualists known to the medical world, and to the world in general, in recent decades.

From time to time their sensational stories appear in the popular Press and are sniggered at—but read avidly—by a large section of the sensation-seeking public.

Trans-sexuality is neither obscene nor is it anti-social.

It is one of life's very real tragedies.

To those men who have successfully taken their place in society after the sex-change operation — and to all those individuals who suffer trial and tribulation through the strange quirk of nature known as transvestism

ACKNOWLEDGEMENTS

The author acknowledges his debt to the authors of works from which extracts appear in this book. Should any material have appeared without permission of the owner of copyright material, acknowledgement will gladly be made in any future edition

By the same author :

MAN INTO WOMAN

SANE AND SENSUAL SEX

HISTORY OF THE ROD AND OTHER CORPORAL PUNISHMENTS

HOW THE STARS CONTROL YOUR SEX-LIFE

CONTENTS

FOREWORD

In a previous book by the author—" Sane and Sensual Sex "
—published by the same publishers of this book, the mysteries of
sex changes in men and women were treated briefly as transvestism
and trans-sexuality and homosexuality came into the general
theme of the book.

In this book—" Man into Woman "—the amazing facts of a
boy child who ended ' his ' days as a beautiful girl, feted by society
and immortalised in the annals of medical history—are written in
stark detail.   For the first time in a text book—details of the
miraculous trans-sexual surgical operation are explained from
beginning to end.

As well—the dark recesses of the child-mind are analysed,
showing the growing conflicts within the young boy's brain as he
grew older, became aware of the differences between boys and
girls—and yearned to cast off masculinity for ever and to assume
the body and the mind of an attractive young girl.

There are homsexualist boys and men, transvestites (cross-
dressers) and trans-sexualists.   Of the three—the trans-sexualist
is the most rare but also the most tragic. The last few decades have
produced examples of men turning into women successfully and
the Press gave increasing space to the news as it realised here was
a marvel of medical and psychiatric science that should at last be
understood by people and accepted as a grave mental and physical
illness of mind and body.

There is a rare and fragile beauty in the female mind struggling, in the male body, for release. The infinite happiness and
transcending joy experienced by the patient when—for the first
time, ' he ' sees ' himself ' transformed into a female, is beyond
human comprehension. In this book—certain sections are devoted
to the intimate thoughts of the man who became a woman—
recorded in the psychiatrist's consulting room—and they give an

insight into the mind of a man who, after years of longing, finally sees the mirrored reflection of his dreams.

On average, people are prone to ridicule the effeminate man, with his feminine traits, ways of walking and holding and using his hands. But little do they know the turmoil of his mind as he goes through life hating his masculinity as if it were a dread disease. Striving, always, to emulate the woman within—trapped in the deepest recesses of his mind.

There have been many female impersonators on the stage, but few, if any, of these have been true trans-sexualists in that they have undergone the vital operation that transforms them from a man into a woman.

These female impersonators wear wigs, false breasts, pad their hips and draw in their waists. But—the type of sex-change man described in this book, after intensive hormone treatment and the final operation—has real breasts, womanly hips and thighs, a feminine waist and long, true, genuine hair. The only things missing are the internal organs of the female that would make it possible for ' him ' to bear a child.

This—medical science cannot create within the man-woman organism. But it can achieve the miracle of transforming a perfect trans-sexualist-subject into a fine semblance of a female, that can defy detection and bring infinite joy and peace of mind to men who have suffered from early childhood from the inward conviction that they have no right to be males—are, in fact, **females.**

This book consists of medical and psychological reports, intimate letters exchanged between the patient and his friends and members of his family. Reports of psycho-analytical sessions between the patient and psychologists and doctors. The over-all picture is a finely detailed account of the agony of mind and body of a pretty, finely proportioned male, richly endowed with surplus female genes—who was a mental and physical misfit in society, and who chose to undergo intense suffering in mind and body to allow the glorious glow of femininity to finally assert itself.

Included in this clinical report is a Personal Questionnaire directed essentially to **men** readers who feel they may also be suffering from certain characteristics that demonstrate the desire either to cross-dress, to indulge in homosexual pursuits or, in fact, to have the courage to accept the final transformation that would change their lives.

Within the hearts, souls and minds of so many men **is** this obsession of the female image which nature has wished upon them and that dogs them throughout life. With the Questionnaire are also supplied ways and means of finding legitimate relief from the terrible desires to cross-dress and to emulate the female, so that, even though a complete trans-sexual change-over is completely out of the question—some measure of relief can be found that will not interfere with society or cross the law of the land.

This book is not only a detailed analysis of the psycho-somatic transformation of a male into a female—but it is also a therapeutic guide to men obsessed with the male-to-female complex, as a means to helping them to live with their obsession and to make the best of the two 'worlds' their Creator has seen fit to give them as their Cross in life.

As such—this book constitutes a valuable reference work and the first-ever guide to happier living for unfortunate victims to the physical and psychological phenomena of trans-sexuality.

INTRODUCTION

There is a half-world in which live men and women of indeterminate sex. This world is a cancer in the heart of society. Misunderstood, abused, laughed at, these folk are at variance with the law. Ill-suffered by the church. Ridiculed by ordinary men and women.

People of this twilight existence cling to one another for solace and release. They are freaks of nature without the ugliness that goes with the word. They have beauty of mind and body. They have intellectual powers, are, more often than not, supremely intelligent and sensitive.

They are not, as the unknowledgeable presume—crude, sensual, perverted. Possessing the physical and sometimes mental attributes of both female and male, they are extra intuitive and emotionally very finely balanced.

Facially, many are handsome. Many are beautiful. Of admirable physique. Keenly aware of music, literature, the arts. Connoisseurs of good food and wine. Houseproud. Lovers of the theatre and the ballet. Tremendously creative, virile—stars in a firmament all of their own.

As conversationalists, they have wit and perception. Life is seen with the tenderness and the compassion of the feminine mind, with the verve and the challenge of the male outlook.

This book is about that half-world.

Perhaps the man who stands next to you in the train each morning is one of these folk of the half-world. Possibly, unknown to you—one of your relatives is a victim. That charming woman you met at that party may suffer the tortures of the damned. Or the endearing young man with poetry at his finger tips craves for the extra depth, the perception and sensitivity of the woman-mind.

And you—yourself ? Suppose such a thing were to happen to **you** ? Is happening at the moment ? Suppose **you** have the wrong body and the wrong mind ? Who do you blame ? Your parents ? Or was it your upbringing and environment that was responsible ?

In the Middle Ages, a woman-man personality would, in all probability, have been burned at the stake as a witch. Are we so very more enlightened today ? Do we not burn the very soul out of such a person we suspect of being, as we like to call it— ' queer ' ?

What good will this book do to those who read it ? Those who are above reproach ? Happy in their one-ness of purpose, their physical and mental perfection ? Perhaps it will help to make them a little kinder. Perhaps the church could grow a little more tolerant. The law more pliable. The State more human.

There are many thousands who suffer from trans-sexual tendencies. Can we fathom the depth of their mental suffering ? Understand the insistent longing for a body different from that with which they have been born ? The attitude to life that belongs to their opposite sex, the deadly dangerous hazards that lie before them if they choose the surgeon's and the psychiatrist's only possible way out of their dilemma ?

Only a very small percentage of the victims of this maladjustment can afford to pay for treatment. Of those who can and do, very few are happy in a complete transformation. Some never survive—so great is the physical and mental shock.

But the few who do come through make medical history. And it is only because the word ' sex ' is involved that these little miracles are frowned upon by the law, condemned by the church and State, mis-interpreted by the people.

A true meaning of the word ' sex ' is a " Fundamental distinction of the organs within a given species into those which produce egg cells (female) and those which produce sperm cells (male) "— WARREN. A strange deviation from the normal and the natural course of events produces the trans-sexual personality. It is as simple as that !

God's laws work in many ways. There is a place on earth— for all his creatures.

Transvestism is the manifestation of a deep-rooted desire to dress in the garments of the opposite sex. When this desire goes further and makes life intolerable because cross-clothes are not enough—bodily attributes of the opposite sex are fanatically desired, a pathological state is created that can result in severe mental disorders.

Because of bigotry and embarrassment the English are prone to turn a blind (but horrified) eye to such things. In the U.S.A., however, a certain understanding exists and these unfortunates are catered for by various bodies and organisations.

On the Continent of Europe, also, tolerance is the rule more than the exception. British conservatism rules that these states of mind and body are taboo and victims are hurriedly thrust out of sight—either in hospitals where they get little to no logically-conceived treatment, or to prisons where homosexuals among the prisoners and the wardens breed even more discontent and confusion in the minds of the sufferers.

Magnus Hirschfield, of the Berlin Institute of Sexology, first coined the term 'transvestism'. Havelock Ellis has preferred the word 'Eonism'—or 'sexoesthetic inversion'.

Women have the best of this bad world insomuch as they are permitted to indulge their taste for masculine attire in public, at will, whereas the unfortunate man has to dress up in private. Venture on to the steets in feminine attire or wearing make-up— and he is arrested as soon as possible.

This unfair distribution of justice is incomprehensible although it is not suggested men **should** parade the streets in female's clothing for, naturally, they can look more grotesque than women in men's clothing and can cause, as the police say— a 'breach of the peace' in next to no time.

Nevertheless, arrest and imprisonment or heavy fines should not be the lot of these individuals.

You cannot persuade a man so obsessed that he must 'be a man'—go and play games, dig the roads up and so on. As few realise, so compelling an urge as to live as a female is no passing fancy, no excursion into fantasy in pursuit of sexual excitement. It is as true and deep-rooted an urge as is the composer's to write music, the author's to write books, the painter's to paint pictures.

Many married men live happily with understanding wives who tolerate—and, in many cases, enjoy and appreciate—their husband's wishes to retire into the peace and quiet of femininity when the day's work is done. Many a man is happy, as a bachelor, in the seclusion of his rooms, to dress as a woman and to spend his spare time outside the masculine body that binds him to this earth.

But with some others, it is so deep-rooted, and so insistent are the urges, so unevenly distributed are the sex glands and hormones, that the desire to **become a woman is a life's ambition**—pursued with diligence until some very real physical and mental transformation has taken place.

GILBERT OAKLEY, D.PSY., 1964.

And Adam said —" This is now bone of my bones, and flesh of my flesh; she shall be called woman, because she was taken out of man ".

Genesis, 2, v 23

PART ONE

EARLY DEVELOPMENTS

1

THE BOY WITH THE GIRL-IMAGE

This is the entry on a Case History Card at St. —— Hospital, Casablanca—filed in 1960. It reads . . .

> *Case No. 6. Julian Griffiths, male. Born November 19th, 1930. Died January 12th, 1960. Sex at death—female. Re-issued Birth Certificate Registers Case No. 6 as . . . Juliet Griffiths.*
>
> *Cause of Death—Suicide.*
>
> *Special Data—Trans-sexualist. Male change to Female.*
>
> *Comments—sex-change operation at 20 years of age, 1950. Completely successful. Hormone treatment, successful.*
>
> *Characteristics—at death. The patient possessed a perfect pair of female breasts and a vagina formed from inverted penis. Complete female characteristics—no facial or bodily hair apart from armpits and pubic region normal and common to female.*
>
> *Natural colouring—fresh female complexion. Dark brown hair in profusion. Vital statistics at death:*
>
> *Height—5'9"*
> *Eyes—brown*
> *Bust—36"*
> *Waist—23"*
> *Hips—36"*

So reads the coldly clinical entry in the files of the Principal of the St. —— Hospital, Casablanca today. And this hides the history of one of the world's most amazingly successful sex-changes in the history of surgery and pathological science.

What you are about to read is the true, intimate account,

compiled from letters from the patient to his brother, friends and
parents, diagnostic dossiers passing from doctors to surgeons to
psychiatrists—of the way in which Julian Griffiths, at the age of
twenty—was transformed into a glamorous girl known as Juliet
Griffiths.

At the age of sixteen, Julian Griffiths was extremely sensitive,
intellectual and of above average intelligence.

He was also an extraordinarily pretty boy.

In a world of males, they were drawbacks. He was of reason-
able height as a boy. But his bones were delicately formed. High
cheekbones dominated his face. At an early age his eyelashes
grew unnaturally long and his eyes were deep-set and dark. Every
gesture, even as a very young boy, was calculated and precise.

As he grew older, these characteristics developed more and
more.

Doctor Hermann Maxfield, of St. —— Hospital, Casablanca,
where Julian's operation took place, has, among the files on the
Julian Griffiths Case—the following notes written by Julian's
brother, who was a Harley Street specialist . . . and they form
the first sections of Julian's amazing Case History.

" With that inate perversity women have for the under-dog
and for the boy who seeks protection and maternal comfort against
the rigours of existence, Julian's mother responded almost immediately to the feminine traits in Julian. She would talk ' woman '
talk to him by the hour. Encourage him in his interests in, and
skill at embroidery. His music she shared with enthusiasm and
did her level best to appear intelligent about his rather unskilled
but very symbolic paintings.

" So I must begin at the beginning which was, in reality— the
end. And the best place to begin is at the edge of a dark lake whose
swirling waters have been lashed into a small fury by a strong
wind sweeping down from the surrounding mountains.

" Here it was the end for Julian. Just a few months before
his thirtieth birthday. His body has been taken from the angry
waters and the wind is cold. Rescue workers are pale in the light
of flares and a small, anxious crowd lines the shores of the lake,
staring down at the slim white body of Julian.

" Then all the difficulty of the inquest. For the body washed
up by the lakeside had been that of a woman. But a post-mortem
had revealed the body had the inner organs of a man.

" The publicity in the Press. The offers from Sunday newspapers for the cold facts.

" But, when it was all over, knowing that Julian was a perfect example of the miracles that can be worked on mankind provided everything is in favour, I decided his story should be committed to medical history. I began work in the room in Harley Street. I had long since lived in my Club in the Haymarket as distinct from making my own home. So my consulting room was both my workshop and my laboratory in which I carried out the experiment of analysing the strange life my brother led in the few short years that were destined to be his, and to add my observations to the complete Case History.

" From time to time patients look at the picture of a very beautiful, dark-haired woman that stands on my desk.

" I tell them that was my sister—Juliet. Because that is just how I like to think of Julian now.

" Some of my patients remember the case and are sympathetic, or marvel in turn. Or are confused. Or incredulous.

" And very, very often I am visited by poor pathetic creatures who think I had some hand in the miracle of Julian, and ask me to help them. People who hover in the twilight world of indecision. They who will never make the journey into complete transformation, for nature has failed to complete.

" My earliest intimation that all was not well with Julian was the day I went into the bedroom we shared as young boys. He was thirteen. I was seventeen. It was a sultry summer afternoon. A slight storm had done nothing to clear the air and clouds of midges in the garden showed there was more thunder to come. I stepped into the bedroom and surprised a young girl with a short white tennis skirt and white sweater, standing in front of the wardrobe mirror. She had her back to me as I entered. I noted shoulder-length black hair, bare legs with white tennis ankle socks and plimsolls. She had her hands on her hips and was swinging her body from side to side, immersed in the reflection of herself.

" I gathered she was a friend of Julian's and went forward to introduce myself.

" At that moment the girl turnd round and, behind beautifully made up eyes, a face lightly dusted with powder, lips brushed with lipstick and cheeks faintly glowing with colour—under all this and under the black hair with the swept-back waves—**I saw the face of my brother, Julian.**

" For a moment we stared at each other—the colour mounting in his cheeks. Julian was tall and willowy. I looked at him from head to toe. And I remember that I was fascinated by what I saw. His face began to pale then and his eyes, dark and liquid brown, looked at me reproachfully. ' You've spoilt it all ', he said, in a low voice.

" ' Spoilt what ? ' I asked.

" ' My game ', he said.

" ' Dressing up as a girl ? '

" He nodded.

" At that moment, my friend Sandra came into the room. She was an auburn-haired girl, a frequent visitor to our house, of which she had the complete run. Hence her unconcerned entry into our bedroom. She stopped short when she caught sight of Julian and was about to leave in what I felt sure was a jealous little huff, when she took another look.

" She stepped swiftly forward, took a long look at Julian's face, then looked him up and down slowly and deliberately. Her face broke into smiles. ' Why—it's **Julian** ', she said. ' And what a perfectly smashing girl he makes ! '

" I saw Julian's face light up at this. Saw the colour mounting his cheeks again. She saw the pleasure he felt in his whole being as Sandra spoke.

" He moved his arms from the front of his body and placed them on his hips in what I felt was a defiant gesture. He looked at me with an air of triumph.

" Sandra appeared fascinated. She didn't say anything for a moment, but fixed her gaze on Julian's thighs, which he had moved together on the instant I moved.

" ' You should have been a girl ', she said. And there was real admiration in her voice. Then she turned and walked slowly out of the room.

" ' Get changed back into your own clothes ', I said.

" ' She liked me ', said Julian, a note of pride in his voice.

" ' Get out of those foolish clothes, for heaven's sake, before father or mother catch you ', I replied angrily. ' And ', I went on, ' As for Sandra—the thing'll be all over town by tomorrow—you see. And we'll be the laughing stock of the place '.

" But Sandra told no one. And, to my dismay, I caught them both in the bedroom the next day, standing in front of the dressing table mirror. She was making Julian's face up. The black wig lay on a chair by the table. I watched, unseen, from the doorway.

" When Sandra had finished, she stepped back to look at him.

" ' That's far better ', she said. ' Now you really **do** look beautiful '.

" Julian smiled back at her, and I looked straight at the face of an indescribably pretty girl, dark eyed, lips beautifully shaped. Even the short dark hair without the wig didn't spoil the illusion. Even the white shirt and long grey flannels helped the effect.

" Then Sandra took Julian in her arms and kissed him.

" ' Tomorrow ', she said, ' I'll help you to dress up. Would you like that ? '

" Julian nodded, his eyes bright with happiness. She kissed him again and, turning, saw me at the door.

" ' How long have **you** been there ? ' she demanded. And I knew, from the tone of her voice, that Julian had completely bewitched her. And that she herself was perverted.

" All that seems a very long time ago. But that was the first time that Julian seduced a girl. To her own image and likeness. And it was the first time **he** had been seduced—to the image and likeness of that which he wished to be.

" In those few appalling minutes, Sandra and Julian had identified themselves with each other. And a strange love affair had begun in which both loved themselves through the mirror of each other's eyes.

" I have often wondered whether Julian would have started his downfall had he never met Sandra. But I have been forced to the conclusion it was inevitable Julian was to go the way he did, Sandra or no Sandra. And, possibly, his first sexual trauma might have been with an inverted youth. And Julian would have become homosexual. For, whatever my brother was, I can say, in all truth, he was never homosexually inclined in the true sense of the word.

" In the early chapters of his amazing change, woman was the centre of his whole existence. But not as man looks at woman. As woman looks at woman. With pride, jealousy, envy, longing. It was not to be for a very long time that he was to look at men. And when he did, he saw man as woman sees man—as the natural opposite member, as the natural complement to her own sex.

" Only very rarely can the expert medical eye see radiant womanhood hiding behind the masculine exterior. The trained mind of the psychologist is able, only on rare occasions, to divine the feminine intellect behind the male mind—seeking release from the fetters of masculinity.

" Before me paraded, after the death of Julian, a succession of hermophrodites, effeminate young men and masculine women, each searching for release from their particular prison. I was struck by how much misery there seemed suddenly to be concentrated in my consulting room, and this, representing only such a very small sum of the total there must be in the world. The act of conception seemed to me, in those moments, a very dangerous and hazardous thing. And I was aware more than I had ever been before of the very great and terrible responsibility of parenthood ".

2

THE GIRL IN THE MIRROR

Among the many notes in the Case History files of Julian Griffiths, kept at the hospital at Casablanca, were scribblings by the young Julian from about the age of twelve onwards—when he first began to be so painfully aware that all was not well with him.

He kept a sort of loose-leaf diary, and, although several pages were either missing from each month or had been left blank, many entries remained to illustrate his fevered state of mind during those early years. Predominant among his aberrations was his interest in his reflection in a long gilt mirror in his bedroom. He spent hours in front of this mirror indulging himself in his feminine fantasy.

In his diary, he would write . . . "I see before me in the mirror a tall figure, whose thighs are rounded like a girl's, without the hair a boy develops at my age. Smooth as marble and white. And there is not that bony prominence that marks the male knees. Instead, my knees are soft and round as also are my thighs.

His waist was slender and small, his hips were unduly rounded. And soft rounds were already making themselves seen in the region of his breasts.

Through half-closed eyes he would gaze at his face which, in the softened aspect seen through his long lashes, would appear as a girl's, with delicate, high cheek-bones and pursed lips. Already, his hair was growing longer and a disarming widow's peak accentuated the fineness of his brow. The black hair was lustrous and wavy.

For a long time he would gaze at this face looking back at him from the mirror.

"I see", he had written in his notes, "the face of a sweet girl, with a cat-like look in her eyes, but with a dark beauty, a sensual appeal that over-rides the cruel look that may flash from

23

her eyes. Her lips are perfectly formed—full and red. Deep shadows lie under her cheek-bones and everything is a symphony of stark white and black and red. I press my lips to the girl in the mirror and feel the icy touch of her lips pressed against mine. I move my body closer to the mirror and feel **her** body, icy cold, touching mine, from lips to thighs.

" Soon, if I stay long enough—her body grows warm as it presses against mine and I know I am infusing life into the girl in the mirror. That she is becoming me and I her. Then strange, exotic sensations begin to surge around my loins and I begin to move imperceptibly against the girl in the mirror. I press closer and closer. Then I move my body and she retreats also. Once again, I press my body close to hers, and the whole of me is filled with a voluptuous feeling that grows hotter and hotter and more and more insistent with each second that passes. In a decisive, culminating wave—this wondrous girl in the mirror seems to melt into me—and I have become her. My whole body vibrates in sympathy with her. I am, at that moment—this very girl who gazes back at me from the mirror ".

Often, Sandra would come into the house and catch Julian at his mirror games. " You **are** a beautiful girl ", she would say to him.

" Sometimes ", Julian wrote to her, " I feel I am **you.** You breathe your soul into me and are transforming my body into yours ".

Then began the long course of hormone treatment prescribed by the family doctor who realised Julian's state of mind and the serious damage that might be done were he not to be allowed to encourage the onset of his feminine tendencies. So he prescribed for him.

He was given folliculin and luetin—the two ovary-secreting hormones. These are responsible for breast-formation in the female. He was also injected with oestradiol monobenzoate in his mammary (breast) glands. Strenuous and continuous daily exercises were called for to exercise the pectoral muscles. He had to have steam baths and cold immersions alternately. Electrotherapy was applied to make his breasts firm. Galvanofaradaic (electrically charged) treatments were administered to condition his chest-area to reconcile itself to the feminine characteristics it was now adopting. Astringents were used to characterise the skin and tissue

qualities of his bosom and massage was applied. This treatment,
gradually, at the age of eighteen or so, made a great change in
Julian's appearance. His hair grew longer, his waist was slimmer,
hips wider and more rounded, as also were his shoulders and his
arms.

But—going back to his childhood and his days at school . . .

Although he had no opportunities for dressing in girl's clothing at the school, Julian was feted by several husky types several
years his senior and used by them in various midnight ' rags ' to
further their own perverted tastes.

Deeper and deeper were sown into his soul the complexities
and perplexities of trans-sexuality.

" My whole being ", he wrote on one occasion, " revolts
against having been born a male. The effort, the toil, the straining
at the leash to find a place in the world, only to have it sacrificed
for the purpose of rearing a family and creating more unfortunates
to carry on the hopeless game fills me with dismay ".

And again, after he had been at school for three terms— " I
am only happy when they (the senior boys) are round me, discussing music and art and good books. Although they invite me
to carry out practices with them I do assure you I do not agree to
to their suggestions. But I am forced to see many games they
play among themselves. But I feel only pity for them. For I know
that deep inside me I am truly feminine, whereas they only play at
it and will never realise the ecstasy of true womanhood as I shall
—one day ".

Julian's brother ran into Sandra one day when Julian had
been at school for some time. They discussed Julian, and the discussion was recorded for the Clinic.

" He is a lovely boy ", said Sandra. " He has the most peculiar
type of sex appeal. I miss him very much. He did something for
me that no boy has ever done. I could stand and gaze at him for
hours. I suppose you blame **me** for the fact that he has been sent
away ? I suppose you think it was me who perverted him ? " she
asked. " But I know I am not to blame. Surely you must see he
is not **like** other boys ? That he never **will** be ? Mentally, he is
far above average. He is poised and cool. He has a tremendous
personality. But surely you see what is trying to force its way to
the surface ? "

Julian's brother nodded.

" Do you intend to help him ? "

" What can I do ? "

" Get him away from that school, where I am perfectly sure he is going through a particular sort of hell ".

" And then . . . ? "

" There are things that **can** be done. Rehabilitation. Re-education. A course of psychiatry. But we can't just let him go on and on. Don't you see what a misery his life will be ? And into whose hands might he not fall one day ? "

" He can be forced to give up his ideas ".

" How do you know how Julian looks at life ? " asked Sandra. " I think **I** am the only person who knows anything about Julian ", she went on. " He has told me everything about himself ".

" Why have you taken such an interest in him ? "

" I am not a normal girl ", answered Sandra. " Or are you so simple you do not see that ? "

" You are certainly pretty cold ', he replied.

" And you are pretty inept as a lover ", she countered. " But you cannot help that. I think you are your father's son and Julian is your mother's son. Or, rather, I should say—daughter. And I recognise that fact because **my** world is full of other girls. You see what I mean ? And that is why Julian appeals to me so much. Why I encourage him in dressing up and help him to make his face up ".

" You want the best of both worlds—the boy **and** the girl ? "

" I'm perverted. Let's face it ", said Sandra. " The secret little things intrigue me. Sex, to me, isn't just the dull process of getting married, having children and settling down for the rest of one's life. That's the very least of it. Any fool couple can go to bed and make a baby. But very few can steep themselves in the mysteries of sensuality that lie dormant in most every man and woman. Like you, for instance ", she said. " Beneath that frown and that solid looking face of yours, and deep down inside that respectable, trim, conservative body are primitive desires and dreams that have been handed down to you through generations of mankind. It is only respectability and convention that keep you from breaking out. Don't tell me you never, but never, let your mind wander—just a little ? "

Looking at Sandra in the half-glow of the summer evening, she looked primitive enough in her flame dress and gold hair. It wasn't too hard to see the centuries falling away from her shoulders —revealing the essence of female sensuality and the dreadful springs of desire that had followed her kind from Genesis.

Not too hard, either, to see in this girl what Julian had most wished from life. Looking at her as he must have done from the depths of his far-seeing eyes and letting his tortured mind dwell on all that she stood for in carnal fulfilment, he must indeed have found an almost divine inspiration and source of encouragement.

" Yes ", he agreed, " I **do** let my mind wander from time to time. But I am more appalled with all the misery and suffering I realise must go on in the world than I am fascinated by its promises and implications ".

" But sex should be universal ", said Sandra. The sun glinted in her hair and turned it to the flame of her dress.

" Sex should not be just an affaire between men and women. Men love men and women love women ".

" Every homosexual affair symbolises one child less for the world ", he said.

" Procreation is a middle-class obsession ", Sandra countered. " The man has his nasty little second of virile triumph and the woman suffers for ever ".

" Woman hardly suffers with the joy of bringing up her child ".

" Child bearing is merely a primitive urge dictated by mutual instinct ", retorted Sandra.

" God Almighty gave woman that urge in order there should be a thing such **as** a world, with **people** in it ".

" He was a poor psychologist if He thought men and women would be content merely to copulate for the sake of making children. Surely, didn't it occur to Him that they would want to experiment ? "

" That occurred to Eve in the first place ", he said. " And Adam wasn't far behind ! "

" I do believe you are sanctimonious ", laughed Sandra. " But you are really rather a dear. And Julian should be very pleased to have you for a brother ".

She grew serious again.

" But I honestly don't think you will ever convert him ", she said. " You must accept the fact that he is not normal. By that, I mean he is not fully male. Face up to it ".

" You mean Julian is an hermophrodite ? " he asked.

" I mean nothing of the kind ", said Sandra.   " Julian is nothing of the sort. As far as male physical attributes go—he is fully developed. He could make a child with a woman as well as any man. But his outlook, his attitude to life is definitely, inescapably **feminine** ".

" But his body—you said it was developing female characteristics ? "

" It is. His body is developing on the lines I have described. But his sex organs are completely male ".

" What is to become of him ? "

" He is an object of great beauty ", said Sandra. " He is like an uncompleted poem. His voice is neither deep like a growing boys, nor is it high-pitched like a girl's. He is mature beyond his years ".

" But you haven't seen him since father sent him away to boarding school ? "

" But I have ", replied Sandra. " I have been seeing him for a long time now. Almost every week-end I called at the school and posed as his cousin, and it became a regular thing for the headmaster to grant him a pass for the week-end so that he could stay at an hotel with me ".

" You are the limit ", he replied. " Not yet out of your 'teens, and you do things like that. I suppose it's all your parents' horrible money and position that have spoilt you ".

" That's it ", laughed Sandra. " But I am fascinated with Julian. And I mean to help him as much as I can ".

" How **can** you possibly help him ? "

" I am the only person in the whole world who really understands him. Look at your fool father. Shutting him away in a boarding school in case the neighbours find out. Trying to pretend he just doesn't exist. And your doting mother playing the witty Victorian grande dame and getting more and more confused all the time. And **you.** What have **you** done to try to understand Julian ?   I haven't forgotten the day I first saw Julian in your bedroom wearing that white tennis outfit. To Julian, there was nothing shameful—**is** nothing shameful—in what he does. Don't you understand ?—trying to transform himself into a girl is a perfectly natural thing to Julian. Living as a male is a far more shameful thing to his way of thinking ".

" Then he is amoral ? "

" That is a harsh word. And most out of place. Julian knows perfectly well what is right and what is wrong. But he thinks it is wrong for him to live as a male and right for him to be a female. If he thinks backwards—that is not the result of an amoral or an immoral outlook. Neither is it a perversion. With true homosexuals there is no knowledgable, deliberate sin against society. So it is with Julian—who is, I believe, what is called a crossdresser, a transvestite and a trans-sexualist "

" What an extensive knowledge of these things you have ", said Julian's brother.

" I've told you—I'm perverted in the true sense of the word. I can make my choice between right and wrong, and I choose to take the wrong road because it intrigues and excites me. But, for Julian, I feel a true compassion and pity. An affinity, if you like. He is not just a weak, effeminate boy with cissy ideals. He is a woman in his mind, and half his physical make-up is female ".

" A freak ? "

" We usually don't hear that word outside the fair-ground ", Sandra said severely. " Your brother is no freak. He is, in fact a quite beautiful creature ".

" Is the rest of the world going to consider him a beautiful creature ? "

" Julian **could** become so very beautiful that the whole intellectual and intelligent world would marvel at the miracle of transformation ", she replied. " When one removes oneself from the confines of suburbia and the rural countryside, and begins to mix a bit with people who **think** for a living—one is able to look at enigmas like Julian with a less biased eye ", she went on.

" And I suppose **you** tear yourself away from time to time from the confines of suburbia and suchlike ? " he asked.

" But of course ", agreed Sandra. " Remember that women grow up far more quickly than do men. Have a far greater questing instinct. Are more adventurous. And are far more likely to be fascinated by sexual aberrations than the average male, difficult though that may be to believe ".

" I always thought men were the dark horses ", he smiled.

" In such matters ", said Sandra, " men are more likely to stop at the physical end of the experimentation. Women, at least women of a certain class and standard of intelligence pursue the

more aesthetic aspects of the matter. They take their sex with a
dash of intellect. They like to enjoy the beauty, the mystery, the
strange sensationalism; to analyse reactions and repercussions.
With the average man, monied, of good class and breeding—or
poor and menial—the end-all and be-all of sex is the moment of
climax towards which he works with a sort of compulsive drive.
Afterwards—he loses interest.   Wants to turn to other things.
Wants to eat or to drink—or to go fast asleep. That is one of the
most successful formulas for an unsuccessful marriage. For
women, the sex act is carried on long after the man has satisfied
himself. Her pregnancy is an extension of her sexual triumph.
The birth of her baby of far deeper signficance than any sexual
climax ".

She continued : " Man thinks he uses woman. But I think
woman uses man far more. And gets more from him in the long
run. And that is why ", she went on, " That is why I think I prefer
women to men. I think men are a little pathetic. So self-assured.
So certain they are indispensable. So very proud of their physical
attributes which are, after all, pathetically powerless as compared
to a woman's ".

Then came a blow one day, when Julian suddenly appeared
on a Saturday morning, complete with his bag and baggage, from
the boarding school. With him he had a note from the headmaster
saying he had been expelled for unruly conduct likely to have a
bad influence on the other pupils.

The unruly conduct had been his appearance one night in the
dormitory in a complete set of schoolgirl's clothes borrowed by
one of the chaps from his sister specially for the purpose of dressing
Juilan up.

Apparently a senior prefect of strong homosexual tendencies
had made advances to Julian, thus clothed, and they had both
been surprised by a housemaster. Although Julian swore there was
nothing sinister in it from his point of view, he had been, nevertheless, held entirely responsible for the whole affair, with
expulsion as the inevitable outcome.

Then began a long and awkward period. Since he was now
seventeen, people began remarking on Julian's girlish face and
appearance.

All this seemed to please him. Far from being offended, he
smiled happily when women stroked his thick, black hair and

made remarks about his slim build and deepset eyes and long lashes. Occasionally Sandra would journey down from town and meet Julian at a small village pub several miles from anywhere. Julian's brother knew this was going on, but he felt powerless to stop it. Eventually he was able to ask Julian exactly what went on between Sandra and himself at these meetings.

"It's wonderful", he said. "In Sandra I see all that I wish to be. She is so beautiful. So feminine. She has a wonderful body and is so warm and understanding".

"But what do you **do** ?" he insisted.

"She teaches me how to be feminine", replied Julian. "And she is giving me hormone tablets to develop me. And a doctor Sandra knows is going to start me on hormone injections soon. The treatment may be wholly successful in a few months, or it may have to go on for years".

"What sort of injections are these ?" his brother asked.

"Luetin and folliculin", answered Julian, unbuttoning his shirt. "Female breasts are formed by them. I will have to have them implanted into me alternately. Also, Sandra tells me I will have to have oestradiol monobenzoate in what are called the mammary glands.

"I shall have to carry out an awful lot of very special exercise every day, so that my pectoral muscles start to work in the right way. Hot baths, hot steam, cold baths and ice packs—all those sort of things !

"And then", he enthused, "I will have to go through a long course of electrotherapy and galvanofaradaic treatments to help the natural reflexes of my chest. The muscles, skin and nerve centres will have become used to doing things quite different from those of the male. And then", he concluded, "there will have to be astringents to tone up the quality and texture of the skin".

Julian got up and began to walk around the room. His brother could see how, when he took off his jacket, his developing breasts stretched his shirt already into two unmistakable points. He wore slim, dark trousers and his waist and hips were, as Sandra had said, finely defined and feminine.

"Then", went on Julian, turning once again to face his brother, "when all that treatment has started to have a real effect on me, Sandra tells me my hair will start to grow longer and to grow more quickly. I shall lose the necessity for shaving, though

I do not have to do that much now, in any case, and . . . " he leaned nearer to his brother " . . . my voice will get lighter and higher, and all its gruffness will disappear ".

Then he went to his bedroom, his brother following. Here, he stripped and surveyed his body in the long mirror. His brother gazed into it with him—and there, without a doubt—was the birth of a girl from a boy.

And Julian's brother remembered how, as a young child, Julian had looked as any other young boy, with a gangling awkwardness of the growing child, with male genitals and everything in order, and wondered at the mysterious change that was now taking place.

3

THE CHURCH'S ATTITUDE

Julian's brother made an appointment to see a priest and one evening he found himself in the study at the Presbytary of the priest's church.

During the course of the conversation they discussed the Nazi outlook before the Second World War, on the question of imbecile children.

" Quite damnable ", said Father Kelly, a youngish looking, fresh-faced individual with a marked Irish brogue.

" You mean, the Church feels children who are born hopeless imbeciles or with some really dreadful deformity or affliction should be allowed to go on living miserable lives ? "

He nodded.

" A liability to their parents, a heavy cross on their shoulders for all their married lives ? " asked Julian's brother.

He agreed that this was the Church's ideal.

" Would it not be more merciful to the child and to the poor parents to have the child put painlessly to sleep before it had time to realise it was alive ? "

" What God puts together, no man must rend asunder ", replied Father Kelly.

" Then God would have responsibility for creating a monster child ? "

" It would have been His Divine Will that it should be so ".

" That the parents should suffer ? "

" Yes ".

" And an innocent child ", went on Julian's brother, " with no sin whatsoever on his shoulders apart from Original sin, should go painfully and tragically through life until the merciful God saw fit to relieve him of his particular cross ? "

Father Kelly spread his hands helplessly.

" It would be Divine Will ", he said.

" But surely, don't you see ", Julian's brother replied, with
some heat, " that it would not be so much a question of Divine
Will as a distortion of the natural biological functions of conception ?   What is there Divine in a mismanagement of genes and
hormones to the point a gross travesty of a human being is created
in the womb of an all-unsuspecting mother-to-be ?   What Divine
act of intelligence has been at work that will inflict a mother and
a father, for life, with such an unhappy burden ? "

Father Kelly smiled faintly. " They would have their reward
in the hereafter ".

" And the unfortunate child also ? "

" Undoubtedly ".

" And it would be a sin to try to defeat this Divine act ? "

" A very grave sin, to which the Nazis bowed when they had
children of that sort killed and the parents sterilised ".

Referring to Julian, Julian's brother said, " So I take it that
to try to change Julian into a woman is also open to grave criticism
on the part of the Church ? "

" If any consenting parties to such an act were Roman Catholics ", said Father Kelly, " they would be excommunicated ".

" And the Church is content for an individual like Julian,
cursed with such a mental and physical aberration as trans-sexual
tendencies, to go through life greatly oppressed, repressed and
frustrated, rather than try to turn him into a happy individual ? "

" Only the strongest medical recommendations would make
the operation permissible ".

" Julian has those, of course ".

Father Kelly nodded. " So I believe ", he replied. " But it is
still the wilful distortion of Divine Will and I, for my part, cannot
uphold it. It would be far better for your brother to offer up his
misfortune as a sacrifice for the sins of the world ".

" But it isn't every man, or woman who can go through life
with such magnanimous ideals ", said Julian's brother. " Life is
too material. Too full of things to be done.   Isn't it rather a
deliberate waste of intelligence and intellect to channel one's
thoughts and actions into such narrow confines ? Such, after all,
idealistic confines ? Julian may well contribute a great deal to
medical and psychological science if the operation is a success.

He may bring pleasure to thousands in the entertainment world. Solace to those in a similar plight to his ".

"Only sensual pleasure ", observed Father Kelly drily. "Thus adding to his sins. And, as for contributing to medical and psychological knowledge—it would merely be encouraging them still further to distort the Will of God ".

"I saw the essential female shining through Julian now, even more ", went on Julian's brother's account of those days. "His face looked older at the age of sixteen. Sophistication of a sort had set in, born of inward, silent suffering. I had difficulty in accepting him now, as a man, my brother, at all.

"A new elegance was in his walk. The way he placed his hands, gesticulated as he talked. His face had a thousand expressions to register his many emotions. Sadly, for me ", went on Julian's brother, "he now seemed even more remote. A certain amount of intimacy of spirit had left. Instead, all he could talk of was the wonderful year to come in which he would cast off, for all time, the mantle of masculinity.

"So much so that, on occasion, he would revel in walking round the flat in panties and bras, with sleek nylons and tiny suspender belt. He wore a caché sex, a French garment favoured by transvestites, which so drew in the masculine member that, under nylon panties, it was practically invisible. Further, he asked Sandra to call quite often. And, on her visits, he would wish to be left alone with her; to talk, no doubt, 'girl' talk. In this, of course, she was willing to encourage him. I asked her what went on those long evenings when I purposely went out, with a bit of a heavy heart, leaving them together.

"'He is in love with me', said Sandra. 'But, of course, I know he is in love with his own image and likeness as a woman. He uses me as his mirror'.

"'Surely, even a perfect operation will not make Julian so completely feminine that the illusion will be complete down to every detail?' asked Julian's brother.

"'Naked', said Sandra, 'Julian will look just like a woman. His breasts will be firm and rounded as they are now. His hips broadened, as they are now. His waist, slim and small as a woman's, as it is now. But his male organs will not permit of conception. He will never have a child. When he tells this to the man he may eventually marry—a visit to a tactless doctor may ruin the rest of Julian's life'.

" 'The doctor may reveal the true facts to the man Julian has married ? '

" 'That is more than possible', replied Sandra. 'A doctor may feel it goes against the grain to let a man think the woman he has married is a true woman'.

" 'But Julian can lie. Pretend there has been an examination. And there need never be one ? '

" 'I cannot see Julian living such a lie', said Sandra. 'I see Julian telling his man the absolute truth'.

" 'Then Julian must never marry', his brother said firmly. 'And we must warn him of the dangers'.

Many such conversations ended in stalemate. His brother began to fear for Julian's future. Whether, in fact, there was a future for him.

In a few years the decisive step would be taken. He would be in Casablanca under the surgeon's decisive knife. Would it be better for him to go on as he was, playing the part of a half-man, getting as much pleasure from that as was possible, but never losing his masculinity ?

One evening, Julian was lying on the settee. His lips glowed with colour, his face was pale and sculptured, eyes beautifully made up, his hair swept back from his high forehead. He was in a particularly inspired mood, and he was talking to his brother.

" Dear brother ", he said, " if a homo were to approach me as a homo, looking for fulfilment in me as a man-woman, I would not let him touch me. But if a man who loved woman as a woman were to look at me, well, then I expect I would be lost. I must be loved by man—as a woman. Otherwise—why make the great sacrifice ? Why be robbed of the fertility and potency beloved by all men ? Why lose the organ by which all men swear and which is the pride of their lives ?

" What have I lived for all my life so far ? To be a travesty of a woman ? I don't want any scented, drivelling homosexual invading my body and using it for his perverted tastes. I would prefer to be seduced by a woman who knew me for a man who was once a man and who delighted in the thought of loving a woman born out of another woman's womb as a man ".

"Don't get so involved", pleaded Julian's brother.

"The whole thing is involved", he said. "By God", he went on, "is there any person on the face of the earth as involved as I am?"

"Plenty", replied his brother. "Yours is not the **only** case of its kind. But others are not so lucky as you. They have not Sandra in their lives, or me, or a kindly doctor, or the hopes of operation. They will have to go on through life living a fantasy and never achieving their goal—to be real women".

"Did you know", Sandra asked Julian's brother on one occasion, "that Catherine Howard, one of the wives of Henry VIII, engaged in tribadistic practices? And that married women do it, in spite of the fact they profess love for their husbands?"

"Are you in love with females?" asked Julian's brother.

"Of course. How else can one know the true meaning of love?"

"But it forms the whole of your life. I know you are so well off you do not have to work. So you devote most of your waking hours to it—isn't that so?"

She nodded. "It is only my sort who do", she agreed. "The working classes rarely do, except, of course, for certain prostitutes who seek happiness with each other as relief from the perversions most of them have to practise with their clients".

"Then money, and idleness and a carefree existence are answerable for your condition?"

"Don't call it a condition", replied Sandra, with some heat. "It sounds as if it was an illness".

"But surely it **is**?"

"That is exactly the attitude that prevents your understanding Julian", said Sandra. "Sex is **not** an illness".

"But perverted ways of applying it surely are?"

"How many mental and physical illnesses have been caused, and **are** caused, by men and women being frustrated and repressed, inhibited to hell because they cannot seek the logical outlook their attitude to sex demands?" demanded Sandra.

"Look at me", she said. "Do I look ill? Look at my complexion. Flawless. See my eyes. Bright, clear, sparkling. Look at my figure. Perfect! Do I look ill? Yet I am 'ill', as you say. You are far more ill than I am, believe me. You lead a celibate existence for no other reason at all than honest-to-goodness fear. You are probably afraid of making a fool of yourself with a woman. Failing at the crucial moment. You have never slept with a woman ? "

" No ".

" But you are not another **Julian** ", said Sandra. " You look one hundred per cent. male. What is the matter with you ? "

" I think ", said Julian's brother, " that when Julian was born, he was given all the sex for both of us. I think he has sapped it all away from me ".

" That is just a state of mind ", replied Sandra.

4

CLINICAL REPORT ON JULIAN—AGE TWELVE

" Julian Griffiths. Age Twelve. Pronounced trans-sexualist tendencies. This boy has an intense desire to change his sexual state and this includes the structure of his body. The patient wishes to function completely as a girl. His state of mind indicates that treatment is vitally necessary as—as he grows older—he is likely to develop a schizophrenic outlook in which the male and female will fight each other mentally and physically.

" The patient is a perfect example of an embryo trans-sexualist. Physical structure indicates the slim waisted, round hipped feminine type. Small ankles and active action in the mammary glands indicate that hormone treatment and injections would cultivate these tendencies to a great degree.

"**State of mind.** This shows a marked predilection for feminine pursuits such as embroidery, sewing, painting and domestic activities. The patient's mind possesses a great appreciation for things of beauty. He is artistic and creative. Boys of his own age have no attraction for him, which indicates lack of any homosexual tendencies. Masturbation has set in—with his reflected self as main object of masturbatory activity. The desire to cross-dress is most marked.

"**Environment.** The patient comes from a good home. His mother has lavished great affection on him. His father is weak-willed insomuch as he appears to have no determination to control his son's destiny. The mother dressed the child in girlish clothes to quite a late age. At the age of twelve, Julian is tall, with fine, shapely legs. The mother persists in keeping him in short trousers so that his legs can be admired by her woman friends. This is accepted by Julian as he appears **also** to be extraordinarily proud of his legs. There is complete absence of boyish down on his thighs, his chest is also completely free and, so far, there is no evidence that he will soon have to shave.

"**Sex Organ abhorrence.** The patient betrays an obvious dislike of his male sexual organs, but is strongly addicted to masturbation. These sessions are accompanied by mirror-fantasies.

Classification of Julian Griffiths' degree of trans-sexuality

Type.	Physical Peculiarities.	Mental Attitude.
A. Extreme.	Pronounced mammary (breast) development. Slim waist and feminine pelvic structure. Lack of hair-producing hormones. Fleshy upper thighs suggest female development. Round character of hips follows this closely.	Male in aggressiveness but decidedly female in almost all other mental attitudes. There is an automatic follow-through of feminine thought followed by feminine action. This is most pronounced in gesture with hands, way of walking and in the general carriage.

"Intersexuality arises from endocrine imbalance or inherited tendencies. The patient has no history in his family of such traits. His father is strictly masculine as his mother is strictly feminine. Psychological origins must be ruled out although they do play an important part. His physical characteristics with their marked feminine tendencies over-rule deeply mental aberrations. Rather is the state of his mind caused by his body rather than the state of his body caused by his mind. Psychological cure, therefore, seems a remote hope.

"Chromosomal sex produces the homogametic female with XX chromosomes or the heterogametic male with XY chromosomes. Disturbances give rise to imbalance that can produce the hermophrodite or the trans-sexual individual.

"Whereas the hermophrodite will possess indeterminate sexual organs of both male and female—the trans-sexualist will have (in the case of a male) all the strongly marked genitals of the male but will seek to disown these in favour of female genital organs and breasts.

"This is primarily a state of mind but is dictated by genetic unrest in the human system. If such a state of mind is encouraged by parents, relatives or friends—it will get a greater grip on the individual. Deliberate frustration or the punishment-element will, however, create a whole new set of complexes and repressions that could prove extremely dangerous to the patient—with possible suicide as climax.

" There was a time ", goes on this report, " in Julian's young childhood, when there was hardly a trace of the mental and physical developments that were to come. He appeared to be a male child, very pretty, with luxuriant hair, long lashes and the complexion of a girl. But all this was taken to be the manifestations of an extra good-looking boy and there were no suspicions of what was to come.

" No doubt the mother was prompted to pamper her boy-child far more than is usual in view of his extreme attractiveness. And most certainly this made her keep him in girlish clothing long past the normal time for such garments. Also, this made her parade her very young son before her female friends, wearing short silk skirts and silk panties.

" Her desire was to keep him from wearing long trousers when he had grown to a height that made them normally desirable. —a perfect example of a mother carrying out a secret ' daughter-wish '. In addition to forcing the boy to display his long legs in extra-short short trousers, she made him wear silk and cotton and nylon underpants cut by herself, as near as possible to feminine patterns.

" At the age of twelve, he possessed a degree of sophistication into these matters that was really quite formidable. In addition— the production and flow of seminal fluid in one so young was a physical phenomenon. Indeed, it seemed (concluded a doctor's report) that the boy Julian would not live to enjoy a long life, either as a male or a female, as he was burning up his bodily energy at great speed and to an alarming degree.

" In addition (went on the report) Julian's mental output was far beyond his years. He seemed to have a tremendously active brain, assimilating facts and figures with the skill of someone twice his age, if not more. He became quite a figure of fame in the countryside in which he lived, although, of course (said the doctor) he was also a figure of ridicule in many unintelligent and mis-understanding quarters—notably in those of the lower orders who could not even begin to grasp the phenomenon of a boy changing into a girl—or even acknowledge the possibility of such an event.

" Sandra was similarly over-developed mentally and physically and seemed to have been created ideally as a foil to Julian.

"" It seemed a natural pattern of events that she and Julian should turn to each other. In fact, it appeared to be pre-destined, for Sandra was to play an important part in Julian's life. She was the projected image of Julian's girl-wish, and upon her he fashioned himself ".

In a discussion between a psychologist and Julian's brother— it was related that the brother had fallen in love with Sandra. But the advances had been repulsed, though Sandra and Julian's brother remained great friends right up until the time of Julian's suicide.

The brother had developed in a perfectly normal fashion, being a normal man, looking like one and having the natural desires of a man. It was quite natural he should fall in love with Sandra, who developed early into a sultry female, the very personification of sex-appeal and femininity.

But Sandra had inverted and unrealised Lesbian tendencies. Instead of lavishing her affections and sexual desire upon schoolgirls or adolescent girls or older women—she concentrated her physical, sexual and mental energies upon Julian—who—to her— represented a perfect union of the male-female, and satisfied her desires for male sexual union plus female sexual union.

Had Julian not been in her life, there is no doubt (remarked Dr. Hersfelt on one occasion) that Sandra would have been an out-and-out-practising Lesbian from a very early sexual age.

Sandra, with her fabulous hair and dazzling good looks, had a perfect figure to match. She dressed in a provocative fashion, and was never at a loss to display her sexuality in short skirts, dazzling underwear and a great show of snow-white legs and breasts. Her lips were full and round, her green eyes deep-set and long-lashed. Her pelvic region was beautifully developed, flaming red pubic hair setting off the glow of her white flesh. Her nipples seemed always to be angry and inflamed, her breasts glowing with the insistence of desire. To Julian—Sandra was a forever-flame burning in his highly-sexed life.

5

THE CONDITION IS UNIVERSAL

There are more transvestites and trans-sexualists in the world than the layman imagines. Some countries are sympathetic towards these individuals—others not so.

Here is part of a report from David H. Keller, M.D., that appears in the book—"Transvestism—Men in Female Dress" edited by David O. Cauldwell, Sc.D., M.D., and published by Sexology Corporation of New York and Wehman Bros., 712, Broadway, N.Y.3 . . .

Many transvestites have written to me (writes Dr. Keller). A man in New York thinks that he is changing into a woman, fears he is going insane, stays in his home secluded from the world, dresses in feminine clothing and is cared for by a loving and sympathetic wife. A man in Iowa leads the life of a woman on an isolated farm, thinks that he is turning into a woman, notices feminine changes in his body, desires to become a mother and nurse a child.

A man from the South writes asking if it is possible by plastic surgery to have all his male organs removed and female organs substituted. A man in Washington works as a man in the daytime, and after office hours wears feminine costume and cooks, sews and decorates his lonely home. A man in New England bosses forty men on a railroad track in the daytime, and at night dresses like a woman, sweeps the house, washes dishes and scrubs the floor. He thinks that he is more of a woman than a man. A man in West Virginia writes concerning the amputation of his male organ.

Twenty-five years ago all these men would have been considered insane and would have been sent to state hospitals. We take a more understanding view of their problems today.

We believe that this man is sick, but we cannot consider that he is insane, says Dr. Keller, in a diagnosis about one particular case of transvestism. Something has gone wrong with his pituitary gland, and it is secreting female sex hormones in a male body. An X-ray study and surgery of the gland might locate the disease or tumour formation. He reacts violently to the suggestion that he might become more masculine if he took male sex hormones to swing the sex balance definitely to the masculine side. **He does not want to become more of a man but rather more of a woman.** He feels that this is what he needs to secure mental ease and complete happiness.

It is difficult to state just what the duty of the medical profession is in such a case. Should he be aided in his ambition to become feminine ? Should surgery or endocrine treatment be forced to make him more masculine against his desire ? Has he a right to live his life according to the demands of his feminine sex hormones ? These are all new problems for physicians to face. But one thing is sure. He is a sick man just as a case of **Addison's Disease** (a gland disease) or disorder of the thyroid or pancreatic glands is a sick man. He should be treated kindly and sympathetically, and should not be made in any way to feel that he is a social outcast, a criminal or a case of insanity.

PART TWO

THE BODY-MIND CONFLICT

1

FIRST APPEARANCE IN PUBLIC

Julian's brother records how Julian first stepped out into the street as a female . . .

"So I knew", wrote Julian's brother, "there was little that could be done for Julian, now sixteen, other than to help him. I took him away from our quiet, conventional, conservative country home, away from the dithering mother and platitude-ridden father, to a service flat in town. Fortunately, with money left to me by my grandfather and a substantial yearly allowance to Julian from his father (who was good enough not to stop it), Julian and I were able to live very well.

"I continued my studies and quite soon qualified as a psychologist. A good friend had been holding rooms open for me in Harley Street and, on a triumphal spring moring, I entered them to take up my practice.

"At first I had Julian working for me as an assistant and general secretary. This did not, however, work out very well. He was consistently restive, could not acclimatise himself to the morning coat and striped trousers our profession demanded, and became bored with the work I set him to do.

"Eventually I released him from his duties and had to leave him to his own resources in the flat when I left for my rooms each morning.

"Things went quite well for a time. I would return each evening to a well-tidied flat and a pleasantly cooked meal. Julian indulged his femininity by keeping the place clean and acting as the ' wife '.

"All this time I was watching him closely, for he was deep into the hormone and injection treatments and was, without a doubt, daily growing more ravishing to look at and more and more female.

"I insisted he dressed in men's clothing whenever he went out shopping or for walks and that he wore no trace of make-up.

"All the same, neighbours talked of his womanly face, his feminine gait. Tradesmen who called wagged their tongues. When we went out together, he was the centre of attraction in the streets and in restaurants. Uncomfortable times were experienced by the both of us on these outings and there is no doubt what went on in people's minds in regard to the two of us.

"Eventually it seemed quite impossible for us to be seen walking together as two men. After many heated arguments, during which Julian was usually reduced to tears, I had to agree to the experiment of allowing him to make-up skilfully, put on a newly-acquired, most natural black wig, don a pretty skirt and sweater, wear nylons and high-heeled shoes, and walk out with me.

"We first tried this on an evening when the sun was setting and shadows were beginning to make dark places in the quiet streets. It was a breathless moment as we stepped out of the entrance hall of our block of flats and walked down the steps into the street

"I had given Julian a close scrutiny before we had left. There was no doubt that, with the now absent dark shave-shadow on his cheeks, his wonderful make-up and his lithe, swinging figure—he was essentially **feminine**.

"As we walked and no one stared in more of a way than people **do** look at an attractive girl with her man friend, my confidence grew, and that of Julian's, also.

"I took his arm and we chatted in low tones, for his voice still had a certain male gruffness. Glancing at him sideways from time to time, I knew how fantastically happy he must be feeling. This was his very first time of facing up to the world in feminine garb—and he was carrying it off with flying colours.

"I had a nice little prepared speech ready in case we should be challenged by any know-all, or by the police. Julian was my brother—a patient under my care. My Harley Street credentials would clinch the matter and my personal responsibility for him would placate.

" But, that very first ti
Everywhere we went for the
No stares. No giggles behind

" Home again at midnig
happiness And I had to admi
Julian had to ring Sandra, wl
her the glad news.

" ' Congratulations, darling
since Julian was eager for me
' Now, very soon, we must arrang
you will be the guest of honou

" I looked at Julian as he pu
taller within recent months. Hi ———— ——es accentuated the
fine lines of his face. His widow's peak showed under the line of
his wig.

" I decided it was time to let his own hair grow longer at the
sides as well as at the back, so that he could dispense with the wig.
If ever a direct challenge were to arise in public, real hair would
help carry the day so much better.

" His lips were perfectly formed. Sensuous and full, defined
skilfully with lipstick. His eyes were growing full and lustrous.
Natural, dark eyelashes shielded them and his eyebrows, always
arched to a peak in the centre, now, finely plucked and pencilled-
in, formed perfect frames to his eyes.

" As he stood with one hand on his hip in the most natural
pose possible, I could see how his hips were swelling visibly,
becoming rounded and soft. His waist was slim, his legs long and
tapering with well shaped ankles. Under the sweater, his breasts
were clearly visible, growing more and more every day.

" He moved with elegance and grace. At this moment, his
eyes were alive with pure happiness. He flung himself into a chair
and poured out a drink for the both of us.

" ' I am so happy ', he said.

" ' And I am so relieved ', I answered. ' If tonight had failed
—the future would have looked dim '.

" Then I told him to let his hair grow long and to finish
wearing the wig as soon as possible.

" I knew there was no going back now. I knew I was to guide
my brother through to the bitter end.

my drink, he looked up at me from the

s, brother ', he said, ' for all you are doing for me.
I can grow my hair long. For taking me out tonight
. For having such faith in me '.

That night marked the beginning of many similar adventures
—every one as successful as the first. We went to theatres and
cinemas together. All the time, Julian evinced not the slightest
desire to form any romantic attachments with either boy or girl.
Indeed, he appeared to be quite sexless, reserving all his energies
in this direction to perfecting himself and the new image and likeness he was creating.

"So many people imagine that such a person is completely
sex-ridden, pre-occupied day and night by sensuality and unnatural
desires. Well might it be with some, but I was happy to see Julian
seemed to rise above this, finding complete fulfilment and freedom
from inhibition in the pursuit of his dominating passion.

"At last came the day when the doctor said Julian had no
further need of intensive hormone treatment. That it would be
necessary only for him to have a tablet or two a day in future.
Now, Julian's voice had lost its gruffness. Now he spoke in well
modulated tones, with a voice undoubtedly feminine but with the
attractive huskiness that gives just that hint of doubt.

"His hair was growing luxuriously to his shoulders, the
widow's peak clearly defined. His hair was blue-black, wavy and
lustrous. His face had settled down to a lovely triangle of high
cheek-bones, a perfect nose and full, shapely lips.

"Much money was spent on his wardrobe. He went out on
his own a great deal and, with great confidence and assurance,
coming home with dresses, separates and underwear.

"Then came the day when a letter arrived from our parents
who had, of course, kept up regular correspondence but never
visited us in town, to say they wanted to see Julian.

"This request could not be refused. So I replied, welcoming
them to the flat.

"As the time drew near for their arrival, Julian was very
composed, not one bit fearful of facing up to them, such a changed
person. While I looked forward to seeing them both, I certainly
wondered what effect the transformation was going to have on
them. Not for one moment did I think they could ever dream of

what a complete change had come over Julian. Perhaps they anticipated seeing a pathetic travesty of a painted doll.

" I planned to break things gently to them, for I was perfectly sure they would not be able to believe their eyes. I would have them on my own for a while and Julian could be out for a walk. Then he would come into the flat and they would both have to take the full force of the impact after I had carefully prepared the ground.

" Julian fell in with these plans with enthusiasm.

" They arrived at last and I had the bright idea of having a studio portrait of Julian standing on the mantlepiece of our living room. This was practically the first thing upon which their eyes alighted when they entered the room. It was a really lovely portrait with a plunging neckline revealing the truly feminine curves Julian now possessed.

"My mother looked at it for a few moments before she spoke. Surely, I thought, a mother could not fail to recognise her son— however disguised he might appear to be ? My father joined her at the mantlepiece and looked at the photograph. He turned to me with a smile.

" ' One of your girl friends ? ' he asked.

" I turned from them, slightly off my stride. I had hoped the portrait was going to break the ice before Julian appeared before them.

" My mother was taking my arm. ' I like to think of you having a nice girl friend ', she said. " Especially since you are away from home all the time now '.

" I looked at them both—and took the plunge. ' That's Julian ', I said.

" I saw them look at each other. Then they both went back to the mantlepiece. Mother took the slender silver frame and looked at it closely. Father looked over her shoulder and I could see disbelief in his eyes.

" For a long time, it seemed, they both stared at Julian's face, taking in the sweeping eyelashes, the arched eyebrows. The delicate lips, the long black hair round to the neck line. I could see the amazement in father's eyes as they took in the all-revealing gown that just hung on to Julian's shoulders.

" Then they replaced the photograph on the mantlepiece.

" I poured drinks for us all. We sat down in the quiet, tasteful, cool room. It was a Sunday evening. A church bell tolled in the distance and homing birds stopped for a second or two on the balcony outside the window. Julian would be in his bedroom—waiting for me to call him in.

" ' What went wrong ? ' asked my father, at length. ' Was it our fault—your mother's and mine ? '

" ' Nothing went wrong that was within your control ', I said. ' You decided to have a child, and that was where your responsibility ended. What happened after had nothing whatsoever to do with either of you '.

" ' But—he looks a beautiful girl ', said mother.

" ' And that's just what he is ', I replied. ' Up to a point, that is '.

" ' What point ? ' asked father.

" ' Sexually—he is still a man '.

" ' That bust, then—it's false ? ' said mother.

" And I felt there was a glimmer of hope in her voice. That the whole thing was going to be shown to be merely a clever masquerade after all.

" ' No ', I said. ' Julian has a properly developed woman's bust. He has a slim waist, the hips and the legs of a woman '.

" ' But he is still a man ? ' repeated my father.

" ' Insomuch as he still possesses the male sex organs ', I said, and hoped they would forgive me for my crudity.

" ' But he is a freak '. My mother was on the verge of tears.

" I put my arm round her. ' That word must never be used about Julian ', I said. ' He is no more a freak than I am. When a child first begins to form in the womb, his sex is quite undecided. It could be a girl or it could be a boy. Female ducts called the Muller ducts and male ducts called the Wolff ducts are both present. Nature turns from one to the other, as it were, undecided as to choice. The embryo quickly reaches the stage when it possesses attributes of both male and female. Then, when the fourth month of pregnancy is under way, balanced hormones at last determine what is the rightful sex of the foetus '.

" They sat forward, side by side on the settee, hardly touching their drinks as I tried, in simple language, to explain the miracle that was Julian.

" ' Now, either the male factor atrophies and becomes non-existent, or the female element disappears. What results is the boy-or-girl development that has been nature's choice. But there never exists a one-hundred-per-cent. male or a one-hundred-per-cent. female. **All** boys are born with female elements in them, and **all** girls have male elements in their physical and mental make-up '.

" I encouraged them to finish their drinks and fixed fresh ones for them.

" ' There are many, many variations ', I went on. ' No individual is perfect. Julian has fallen into the category where the female hormones have influenced the secondary sex characteristics to such a degree that Julian has, up to recent years, lived with a woman's mind and outlook in a male body. Obviously—this could not go on if his sanity was to be preserved. If he was to be saved from committing crimes against society that would eventually land him in serious trouble '.

" ' You mean—soliciting men—and all that sort of thing ? ' asked my father.

" ' Not exactly. Julian is not homosexual by any means. I have observed his sexual motivation over these recent years, and it is obvious he is intent on one thing only—the perfection of himself as a **woman**. So that he is accepted by society **as** a woman. That the law and the State grant him the legal status of a woman. After that—there is no knowing how his sexual urge will develop. Naturally—with the mind of a woman—and the entire and complete body of a woman—he is likely to centre his emotional life on females. Which is as it should be. That won't make him homosexual, however '.

" ' The entire and **complete** body of a woman ? ' asked my father. ' What do you mean by that ? '

" I took a deep breath. ' I can see ', I said, ' that Julian will not be happy, or be able to lead a straightforward life, until he has had the final operation '.

" ' Operation ? ' almost whispered my mother.

" I nodded. ' There is only **one** ultimate end to a condition as rare as Julian's ', I said. ' He must become a **complete** woman. Unable, of course, to bear children. But with the outward and, to a point, the **inward** characteristics of a woman. To achieve this will cost a great deal of money. But it will buy happiness and fulfilment for Julian. And this he **must** have, at **all** costs. Otherwise, I do not know what is to become of him '.

" My mother and father looked at each other, then back at me—with the single thought uppermost in their minds. ' What will the world—**our** world—say to all this ?'

" ' Does it **really** matter what the world, ours or anybody else's, says ?' I asked.

" This is **our** world. Yours, mother, yours, father—and mine. Public opinion does not matter. What matters is that Julian should be completely happy. That this peculiar illness of his should be cured by the best means possible. Here, in England, his condition is looked upon as peculiar, to say the least. But the Press and the public are intrigued beyond measure when people like Julian are brought to light—their secrets revealed. I will not pretend that if Julian **does** have the final operation to transform him into a woman, that the whole world will not get to hear of it eventually '.

" ' Terrible ! ' I heard my father say, half to himself.

" I turned to him—angry for the instant.

" ' What is terrible ? ' I demanded. ' That your friends on the Stock Exchange should get to hear of it ? That your social circle back home should snigger behind their hands ? '

" Mother laid a restraining hand on my arm. ' Father does not mean that ', she said. ' Naturally, as a public figure, it would have repercussions on him '.

" ' No one need know ', I said. ' Julian **as a man** can just disappear. In his place can rise **Juliet.** Whether or not you claim **her** as your own flesh and blood is your own affair. Personally, I shall be happy to know her as **my sister** '.

" My father coughed over his drink. ' Can't we arrange for Julian to be sent abroad ? ' he suggested. ' I will willingly pay for his upkeep until he finds some sort of a job—or something. Somewhere abroad, where they understand these—er—sort of things, he will be safe. I will make him an allowance—I promise you '.

" I looked at mother, to see how she was taking all this. She looked tearful. ' We can't **possibly** send him out of our lives **altogether** ', she said. ' After all—he **is** our son '.

" At this moment Julian, grown impatient, no doubt, appeared in the doorway, which he had opened so softly, no one had noticed. He wore a tight white sweater and a short black skirt. His hair framed his pale face. His eyes were dark and anxious. He stood there, hand on the door handle, lips waiting to smile, to speak, to welcome his parents.

" Mother and father turned on the settee and followed my gaze as I looked at him.

" The air was heavy with suspense as they took in the tall, trim figure, searched that face for a glimpse of the teenage boy they had last seen at our home in the country.

" They saw a perfect looking girl. A sweet, sad face, infinitely feminine and appealing. No gross caricature. No painted doll, no travesty of a female.

" And, as this person closed the door and walked towards them with a slow, swinging stride, hips swaying, trim waist as pedestal for proud breasts, eyebrows arched in query and quest for tolerance and sympathy, mother rose and went towards this child. Took him in her arms. Embraced him. Led him to the settee, to sit between her and father.

" And I knew the crisis was passed.

" Father, with that awkward embarrassment a man of his calibre displays in emotional crises, shook Julian by the hand and muttered something quite unintelligible under his breath.

" I viewed this scene dispassionately.

" A mother, father, and their son—dressed as a girl. Slim legs in nylons. Trim ankles and, below, high heeled shoes. A short, black skirt revealing rounded, feminine knees. Obvious, sensual womanhood beneath the tightly-stretched black sweater.

" And now—Julian spoke in that fascinating low-sweet voice. That indeterminate tonal quality that baffled the listener. That was, in reality **all-woman.** More woman than woman herself.

" My parents listened, fascinated and entranced, as Julian greeted them. Told them of the long-drawn-out hormone treatment that had resulted in him perfecting, to this stage, the feminine aspect they now beheld.

" I divined, by the look on my mother's face, that she caught, here and there, now and again, glimpses of Julian's boyhood, when she would secretly encourage him to be girlish, comb his hair, give him dolls to play with and generally pretty him up. Perhaps a pang of conscience passed through her as she looked at Julian and saw in him what subconsciously she had tried to make of him so many long years ago. And no doubt she thought of her wishes to have a girl-child and wondered, perhaps, if pre-natal influence had not had some bearing on the matter.

" As to father, perplexed and embarrassed in turn, what were his thoughts as he looked at the son he had hoped would be good at games, Captain of the School Eleven ? A man keen on golf, with whom he could have enjoyed many a pleasant round at week-ends ?

" Deeply sorry for them both, I explained, as best I could, the depth of their child's problems. Obviously, they had not expected so great a transformation or known the drastic steps Julian was planning to take to perfect the dream that had to become a reality.

" Pleasant conversation was impossible under the present circumstances.

" Father and mother were pleased to know I, personally, was getting on so well. That my Harley Street practice was growing week by week. I think I **also** was now a stranger to them both, though. Julian and I were beyond their plane of existence. Me with my job of probing into human nature, unravelling lost minds and sorting out the complexities of existence. And Julian with his fantastic double life.

" Indeed, after they had left, I think they must have felt they had lost both their sons for ever. I visualised them returning to their prosaic existence, their lovely country house, their parochial and social commitments, their amateur dramatics and bridge parties—hopelessly bewildered with the unparalleled turn of events that had befallen Julian and myself.

" Father had always hoped I, also, would become a Stock-broker and join him in the game of making and losing money over and over again. That Julian would become a barrister and be called to the Bar. Or be a business executive. All the things so beloved of country born and bred stock.

" And mother had harboured happy thoughts of my making a ' successful ' marriage to some country girl with money, family and position. And, no doubt, she thought that sooner or later she would have to surrender Julian to the arms of a woman other than herself.

" Instead, although I was a Harley Street Specialist, my work savoured of the unknown, I mixed with doubtful company in my pursuit of knowledge in order to help me help my patients. And there seemed little hope of my marrying and settling down in the comfortable and reassuring way beloved by so many mothers.

" And Julian—well—Julian was beyond her reach for **ever.**

For she could not accept this pseudo-girl child for her own. Baffled and bewildered, from that moment on, I knew she had disowned Julian for ever in her heart. She just could not reach out to him any more. In spite of the fact she had embraced him when he had first entered the room. But, at that moment, the full import of the situation had not reached her. She had thought he was merely masquerading. The physical side of the thing had not struck her. But, after—it was altogether too enormous for her to grasp.

" Happily, Julian was not much affected by his parents' ultimate coldness or their air of finality.

" As for father—for a man with so many responsibilities on his shoulders, so lacking in a sense of humour, so ponderous and ' old-school-tie-ish ', the thing was completely beyond him. On leaving, he had not known whether to kiss his daughter or to shake hands with his son. His leave-taking was embarrassed. None so the less with me, for he considered me part and parcel of the situation; felt sure, I know, I was encouraging Julian when I might have **discouraged** him.

" However—all parents and offspring have to go their ways eventually. Pleasantly or unpleasantly. This was our particular parting of the ways.

" For myself—I only felt pangs of conscience many months later, when Julian and I learned our parents had both been killed in their car on a Continental tour. But, with Julian, as if a load-stone had been taken from his back, his vitality and personality, his determination to realise his ambitions became, suddenly, threefold.

" And I knew his mother had been a weight on his conscience. His father a vague voice telling him ' thou shalt not '.

" Now, there was only myself left in his life—the only person who really mattered.

" And, in me, he had implicit faith ".

2

EXTRACTS FROM JULIAN'S DIARY

From the age of twelve to twenty-eight—Julian kept extensive Diaries in which he recorded his gradual change-over from boy to girl —man to woman. These Diaries are now in the archives of St. —— Hospital, Casablanca, where they contribute to the large Dossier held there on the Julian Griffiths Case History.

From time to time they are used as references in similar cases of transvestism, but no account of the transformation has yet been so complete as is that contained in Julian's Case History. His Diaries number twenty-eight volumes in all. The last two years of Julian's life have no Diaries, but scores of letters he wrote during those last two years of his troubled life bear testimony to his state of mind.

" Today ", wrote Julian, " Sandra and I went for a bathe in the little cove on that sandy stretch of the beach we seem always to be able to keep exclusively to ourselves. Sandra was in high spirits, most loving towards me, and looked more radiant than I have seen her look for a long time. She wore a short white pleated skirt—the very personification of femininity—and a tight black sweater that showed off her figure to perfection.

" I wore my favourite tight black jeans that Sandra said revealed my hips and my waist best of all. Into them I had tucked a short white silk shirt.

" We walked to the beach and from there to our special cove. As usual, there was not a soul in sight. We had a transistor radio with us and soft music drifted away across the golden sands and lost itself in the high cliffs that surrounded us.

" The sun was delightfully hot, the sky clear blue. The tide was making its way in and, on the distant horizon, a lazy ship seemed anchored for ever in the hazy blue sea.

" Sandra was the first to get undressed. In a second or so her skirt was round her ankles and she was stepping out of it. She stood there, in tiny white panties—her black sweater still on, and,

56

with her red hair streaming from her head like tongues of flame, she was Woman—from Genesis itself.

" She turned to me and told me to undress.

" Soon, we lay side by side in the warm sand. And here I was —a **girl**—with Sandra !

" ' Well ', said Sandra, ' as a girl you know you have the whole world in the palm of your hand. You know that all men are sub-servient to you. That you can get anything you want from them '.

" ' But how does it feel to wear soft dresses and skirts ? "

" Sandra smiled. ' That **is** a great feeling ', she said. ' The feeling, as she walks, that she has nothing on, even though she has, of course, is really quite delightful '.

" Sandra turned to look at me as I bent over her, naked, in the sands, beside her. ' And so you **will** have all those feelings and sensations one day, darling ', she said. ' One day you will be a **complete** woman, and will feel and enjoy all that a woman feels and enjoys about her sex.

" 'Anyhow ', she went on, ' there are times, now, at home, and when you go out dressed as a girl, that you must surely feel all these things ? '

" I nodded. ' Yes, that's true. I **do** feel these things on those occasions; but I know that, until I have my male organs completely removed—I will never feel **completely** feminine '.

" She put her hand on my arm as she lay, looking up at me.

" ' Soon ', she said, ' Soon, that wonderful day **will** come ! ' "

A psychiatrist's analysis of this particular facet of Julian's imagination diagnosed it as a sexo-schizophrenic traumatic phase —thus adding a new psychological term to the science of the mind.

A medical report at the same time stated—" Julian has very pronounced female sex characteristics and his male-female hormone balance is therefore greatly upset. Injection of female hormones into his body have lessened male attributes and have stimulated glandular activity towards creating and encouraging and developing the dormant but persistent female element.

" It would be criminal, at this stage, to cease the treatment and impossible to restore complete male hormone content by introducing male hormones into the system.

" Were this to be done—it would not be possible to rule out or to cancel out the mental attitude of the patient—which is so predominantly female. The death-wish might well result if his persistent feminine characteristics were pushed into the background.

"I therefore prescribe more and **continued** treatment of female hormone injections, together with all attendant therapies aimed at effecting as complete a sex-change as is humanly possible ".

At that stage, an operation for the removal of Julian's male organs had not been envisaged. This was to follow later, when doctors and mind-specialists attending his case would be made to realise that—for his complete peace of mind and to make his life bearable—it would be **necessary** to take the risk.

And risk it would be, of course.

Complete removal of a man's sexual organs is a dreadful shock to the physical and nervous system. So dire an operation is it that it is forbidden by the Church and by the law of practically every country in the world.

Criminal proceedings could be taken against any surgeon performing the operation were it to be unsuccessful and result in the death of the patient. In addition to that, a man so operated upon, if he recovered, could be mentally unstable for the rest of his life and become a menace to himself and to society.

There is, again, the ethical point of the symbolic destruction of a man by removing his sexual organs, the deprivation to the world of a potential father and to a woman a potential husband.

Fifteen years imprisonment could easily be a penalty for such an offence.

However—in extreme cases—and where doctors and magistrates are in conclave—and an unanimous decision to operate is reached—a man **does** have such treatment. If the operation results in death—this is then due to misadventure and no one is held responsible. The operation, from a legal point of view—is looked upon as a form of mutilation.

The law, also, gets very involved in such a case in regard to the man's birth certificate—which has to be re-issued stating ' he ' is now a ' she '.

A whole host of complications arise.

But the very root of the matter is the human one of **preservation of the man's sanity.** For the trans-sexual state of mind is bordering upon insanity and the trans-sexualist state of body borders on malformation and becomes, in a sense, a deformity.

This state of mind and body is a definite ' condition '. An illness of the physical and mental make-up. As such it is worthy of treatment. ' Cure ' is, of course, out of the question, insomuch as it is not possible to turn the man's mind backwards so that he no longer wishes he was a woman. Once such a thought is inherited or implanted in a man's mind—supported by strong female characteristics—there is a pretty hopeless case.

3

JULIAN TAKES TO DRUGS

Following is a taped recording of a psychoanalytical session between a psychiatrist of —— Clinic, London, and Julian. This took place when Julian was sixteen and he was under the influence of the truth drug at the time the tape was made . . .

" Why this confusion of mind and body ? " his voice said on the tape. " And then I delight in thinking of the soft, sensual female form. The walk of it. The way it sways from side to side in motion. The elegance of the moving breasts, the sway of the hips and the roll of the thighs.

" But . . . in a moment, I am full of the glories of masculinity and revelling in my role as a man. The way I can dominate women. The way women hanker after me because I am a man . . . and they know what I can do for them.

" There is a divine inspiration in the creation of the female. And I am part of that inspiration. But I am a man and I am a woman. I know the pleasures of the flesh of both sexes. How can I decide which pleases me most ? I think that the male form revolts me—the flexing muscles, the enormous chest, the matted hair upon the chest.

" Compare all that with the poetry of a woman's body. The soft, smooth, hairless curves. The mountains and the valleys. The swooning passivity of it. The doorway to heaven that opens when response is high. The erectile nipples that guard the streams of life. The rounded flesh that fashions the hips and the thighs. The infinitesimal waist that, like a living hour-glass, completes the human female form.

" Eve was the first woman to be created. Eve knew her charms, the fatality of all that she had to offer to the world. And when she was face to face with Adam for the very first time, all the desire in the world that was to follow for generations to come was there—at that very instant.

"Sometimes I feel that I cannot go on. That it would be better to die, here and now. While womanhood still rests unquietly within my body, soul and mind. Yet something deep within me urges me to go on. That the day will come when I am fully and truly woman. These insistent urges within me cannot be denied forever. There are two of us—boy and girl—man and woman. Surely we were born together, and the day will come when one of us must die—leaving the survivor to glory in his or her future on earth?

"When alone—or with Sandra, and dressed in female clothing from top to bottom, a great peace steals over me that is past my comprehension. I feel, at these moments, that I am truly fulfilled. I am a male, standing outside of myself looking at myself. Here is a tall, dark, lovely young girl, with budding breasts, hips and waist and thighs that form a symphony of soft, resilient, succumbing flesh. Here are delicate, high cheekbones. Rich, black hair. Fragile shoulders and long, tapering legs. Here are lips, beautifully formed—and arched eyebrows and long, sweeping lashes.

"Who am I to deny these things? To prevent this image of all-woman from breaking through the male shell that surrounds it? Yet—the whole world, at times, seems to be against the grand illusion that could become a reality.

"At whose door shall I lay this tragedy? At my mother's—who treated me as a girl for so long in my childhood? Who dressed me in girls' clothing until I was nearly of school age? Who made me go around at school in short pants to a late age—when I was tall and my thighs were growing feminine? Who pinched in my waist with a wide black belt so that all could see how female I was? Or my brother—who derided me for my feminine ways for so long—until—one day—he understood? Or my father, who spoke in his low, gruff voice, of cricket and football, and playing the game and being a man?

"Or is it Sandra—who, with her strange love—encourages me to dress as a girl, buying me girls' clothes, dressing me up in them and making love to me as if I were a girl?

"Are all these people wrong? Or am I right?

"Am I—after all—a true girl with the misfortune to have

been born with a vigorous male member ? Am I a freak of nature who, in the Middle Ages, would have been burnt at the stake ?

"And will I have the courage to suffer the operation that will destroy—for ever—my male organs, and turn me into a woman once and for all and for ever ? "

This tape was played back to Julian—as were many others he recorded in the consulting room. He would ask for it to be repeated time and time again. And, the psychiatrists noted—a dream-like look would come into his eyes as he listened. He would grow to look more and more feminine as the tape played on.

There came a time, however, when Julian grew restless. He had been told that he would not be able to have the vital operation—if ever—until he was at least twenty. The physical and emotional shock would be far too great for him to bear until he was of that age.

So—he resorted to taking drugs and stimulants.

His brother was in the habit of allowing him to go to parties on many occasions. But—one day, Julian's brother discovered that the parties were getting more sinister, that they involved the taking of drugs.

Julian's brother filed a report of this on tape, in secret, with Julian's doctor and psychiatrist. Here is a transcript of that tape :

"A few months after I had given Julian the doctor's verdict of the long wait before the operation, and he had seen the doctor to fill in the necessary forms to forward to the specialist in Casablanca, I discovered to my horror that Julian had begun to take drugs. More correctly, he had got in with a set who had nothing to do with Sandra's lot, and was going to dope parties. I learnt about this through Julian's carelessness in leaving around the flat some notes he had made.

"One particular night he had left for one of his parties that I took to be the usual sort of thing Sandra was in the habit of cooking up. I was clearing up in his bedroom when I came across a sheaf of papers with a recent date on them. In Julian's clear, concise handwriting, set out in his Diary, was an account of a party he had been invited to.

"After looking quickly through the closely written pages, I went to the living room, put a fresh tape on the recorder and sat down to read aloud the disconcerting events Julian had committed to paper. My voice came back to me, translating Julian's experiences :

" ' I have been to another of Adrian's gatherings ', Julian had written in his Diary. ' This time, I tried something a little bit stronger. I was warned its effects were pretty potent. Did it really matter ? There still seem to be a million and one days before there is the slightest hope of the miracle being performed. A million and one days more before I can really look the world in the face and be, for ever—what I want to be.

" ' Tonight, I took a little cantharides, a drug we get from the Spanish Fly. Adrian took me to a little dark room with a red light and a pink ceiling. There, I lay on a soft, low bed and he administered it to me. It was a white, powdery substance and all was well for a little while.

" ' From somewhere came soft music. I knew it was real music. Something quite electronic, the music—concrete sort of thing. Then my throat began to burn. A mild panic surged up in me. I struggled from the bed and made for the door. It was locked. So back to the bed with the burning sensation getting worse and worse.

" ' I lay down again. The burning feeling was now growing into a pain, all down my back and into my stomach. Like a fire in the middle of me.

" ' Then began the most awful impression that I was suffocating. My hands were growing weaker and it was difficult to raise them to my throat to try to stave off the burning sense of choking. Almost as if my throat was closing up. That never again would I be able to swallow, or to let even a trickle of water down my throat.

" ' Then the disgust of vomiting in that small red room, the ceiling now a fiery flame of space above me. But that passed soon enough, leaving me as weak as water. Then griping pains in my stomach. And more vomiting.

" ' I saw with real panic it was now blood. What had Adrian given me ? He had promised me a mild aphrodisiac. That I would have sensual dreams. That my body would fill with the most delightful desires and sensations.

" ' But I had none of these. Instead, I passed out. Which was a mercy. Hours later, I expect, I awakened. Adrian was standing over me '.

" The rest of the page was blank. But, overleaf, was another account of yet another party at which Julian had taken drugs :

" ' My body became suddenly extra-sensitive ', went on Julian's account, as I read it into the mike. ' All sensation is madly magnified. The prick of a pin is delightful anguish. If I pinch myself—the pain is a delight that throbs quite unreasonably through my whole being. Then I palpitate like a woman. My heart flutters and it is difficult to breathe.

" ' Tremors pass through me. The space in front of me becomes filled with delightful, indeterminate beings.

" ' This is intoxication of love. For all in sight is now loved. The pillow upon which rests my head is an object of passion. I cast off the coverlet that is draped over my naked body for this, too, is too much and becomes an insistent and pressing lover upon me.

" ' Music fills the air. But I can determine none of it clearly. It is all the symphonies of the world in one great cacophony. The figures start dancing in front of me and I am filled with the desire to dance as well. But before I can get on my feet I am forced back by some weighty power beyond description, and remain on my bed—immovable '.

" I stopped reading aloud and switched the tape recorder off.

" Clearly, Julian was going to do a great injury to himself if he went on in this way. The deadly effects of the drugs would begin to tell on the finer mechanism of the hormone treatment. There was no way of knowing how the two elements might conflict and ruin all Julian's chances of a successful operation when the time arrived.

" I read through the remainder of his Diary, feeling too sick at heart to make more recordings. When I had finished—I rang the doctor and told him briefly of this latest development.

" ' He must be stopped at all costs ', agreed the doctor.

" Julian was sent to a small private nursing home run by the doctor. Here, Julian underwent a rigid course of treatment to cure him of the drug habit. I went to see him twice a week. The doctor said he had been rescued just in time to prevent the drugs ruining him physically and completely destroying the hormone treatment.

" ' A little while longer ', said the doctor, ' and Julian would have been quite beyond the pale as far as the transformation is concerned. He would have so physically undermined his constitution that the operation would have been very dangerous. The shock to his nervous system would have remained with him for ever instead of, as we hope, fading into his subconscious with the passing of time.

" 'Physically', the doctor continued, 'I think Julian would have developed into a semi-imbecile, with the remains of his femininity hanging on, as it were, to his male make-up. The result would have been a pathetic travesty of man-woman'.

" 'Julian was running away?' I asked.

" The doctor nodded. 'He took the long wait very much to heart. He was prepared to destroy everything the future held, all that had been done for him in the past, rather than face up to the period of waiting for the operation'.

" 'Then that betrays a weak facet in Julian's character'.

" 'All strong men have a moment of weakness', replied the doctor. 'Indeed, if they did not betray a certain weakness from time to time, they would not be able to maintain their inherent strength of character. In temporary weakness, they gather forces together for a renewed and more powerful attack on adversity. This, I feel, has been the case with Julian. He will emerge from his ordeal more determined than ever, to see his great problem through'.

" For months, ever since I had become aware of Julian's regression into the world of drug-addicts, I had feared greatly for his sanity. I suffered with him and for him. And forever before me was the image of his face—an eternal female that sprang from the same loins as those from which I myself had been created. A female who had occupied the same womb as I myself.

" Yet his original masculinity haunted me at the same time and I tried to pry into his secret mind. Wondering how he felt about the mysteries that went on within his unique body and mind. Tried to identify myself with the thoughts that were his in the long quiet hours of the night when he wrestled with his maleness and reached out for the female within.

" Later, when Julian seemed to be making good recovery, I spent hours walking round the grounds of the Home with him. On one occasion he seemed particularly troubled with the religious aspect of his problem.

" 'I seem to see the sign of the cross', he said. 'If a pattern has within it any semblance of the cross—it immediately makes

itself apparent to me.   The criss-cross of window panes.   The
panelling in doors. The lattice-work round this garden. I pick out
crosses in the walls, in patterns on the wallpaper. Then I think—
at times—of sentences with the word ' cross ' in them. ' Across the
road ', ' cross with me ', ' cross your bridges ', ' noughts and
crosses ', and so on '.

" ' You are suffering from a word-obsession ', I said. ' Nothing
to worry about '.

" ' But it all started after a priest came to see me here ',
replied Julian.

" ' What did the priest have to say to you ? '

" ' I put the whole thing to him. This man-woman problem '
said Julian. " And he was aghast. Appalled. ' A sin ', he said,
' against the Almighty. Unnatural. A prostitution of the sacred
Temple of the Soul '. He meant the body, of course '.

" ' Go on '.

" Julian crossed his slender fingers over his lap. ' The priest
said Man was made in His own Image and Likeness. That it was
sinful to try to change God's will. That I was born a man, and
man I should remain. He told me to go to confession. He tried to
convert me to his faith. And ', finished Julian, ' Ever since then,
I have begun to wonder. Am I committing a sin ? '

" ' Nothing that is a pathological compulsion is a sin ', I said.
' A man or woman might visit the confessional time and time
again and confess an aberration, a perversion, convinced it was
a sinful act. But psychological disturbances are not sinful. Indeed,
everything a confessor tells a priest and looks upon as a sin—has
a psychological significance and explanation '.

" ' Then ', said Julian, ' All sin is a pathological condition ?
And being completely sinless is the priest's and the psychologist's
dream of a perfect human being ? '

" ' I would say ', I replied, ' That the completely sinless
human being would be the psychologist's biggest problem child.
It is impossible to live without committing some sin some time or
other. If one does not sin, how is one to know the difference
between right and wrong ? '

" ' But the saints ? ' asked Julian. ' They were not sinners '.

" ' They were. Indeed they were. What about Saul, who
persecuted God ? What about Mary Magdalene, who washed
Christ's feet as an act of contrition for her sins ? But the church

has made many mistakes where saintliness is concerned. Flagellists, for instance, have been considered saintly by the church because they did what was considered as a penance for their sins, and for love of God. They wore hair shirts, fasted, imposed upon themselves many little tortures and discomforts. And, for that, they were looked upon as saints. Today, of course, modern psychology analyses such acts as those of sadists and masochists. Self-imposed torture, discomfort and suffering is a pathological disorder with a sexual origin. Flagellists abound to this day. Flagellism is a masochistic sexual act. A man flogs a woman, and vice versa. Between them, they have committed the sexual act. This is no virtue. This is no saintly act. But, in biblical days— they would have been called saints '.

" Julian listened as I continued : ' In the days of the Inquisition when, for instance, Joan was burnt at the stake—sadism was rampant. This was no devout act, no sentence passed on Joan and witches in general, on heretics and so on for **love of God.** It was pure sadism. Sexual in origin and sexual in intent. And the mobs who watched the burnings, like the mobs in Marie Antoinette's days who flocked to the guillotine, were indulging in sadistic sexualism en masse '.

" Then ', asked Julian, ' I am not to be influenced by what the priest said ? '

" ' I would not belittle a minister's philosophy ', I replied. ' But I have always felt that, in spite of the wise counsel the average priest may give, he is so divorced from the world of reality that one cannot hang too closely on his words. It is one thing to sit in the confessional distributing spiritual largesse, but quite another to be out in the world, overcoming its temptations. . Naturally, to a priest, the trans-sexual operation would be quite horrific. Apart from the physical mutilation of the Temple of the Soul, as your priest put it, a man is being robbed of his ability to make children —a sure sin in the eyes of the Roman Church. Even to the point of imbecility, children **must** be made in order to people the world with scores and scores of little Catholics. This outlook I cannot reconcile with religion '.

" It was interesting, if disturbing, to note the phases through which Julian was passing during this time of his life, before he underwent the operation.

" First, the temporary addiction to drugs, which we had successfully checked before it was too late. Now, in the Home, this predilection for religious mania. I wondered by what unfortunate sequence of events Julian had been visited by the priest. I soon found out when I asked the assistant under Doctor Spenser. Apparently the priest made a habit of visiting patients by arrangement and had effected quite a few conversations in the course of years. I shuddered to visualise Julian's state of mind if, during a course of such visits, he became converted and found himself in a seminary for young priests with his transition from man to woman still incomplete ".

(The priest in question was the minister whose opinions were related in Chapter 3, Part 1—" The Church's Attitude ".)

Here are two extracts from the book, " Transvestism ", edited by David O. Cauldwell, SC.D.,M.D., and published by Sexology Corporation, New York. Medical and psychological opinion is of considerable interest when compared with the Julian Griffiths Case.

" In extreme cases of eonism, where males have dressed as women in public and private, and have lived as completely as possible the life of a woman, they still have had sexual desires for women. They perform the masculine sexual role with a woman as successfully as the average male. Sometimes they are more successful, because they understand the feelings of women better. They certainly are **heterosexual** and **not homosexual**! If eonists were ' unconscious ' homosexuals, they would **not** be heterosexual, or they would have difficulty in being so. If they were homosexual, they would not desire the company of women as they do. Perhaps it would be more correct to say that some homosexuals are eonists, and that some eonists are homosexual. We all have some degree of the **opposite** sex in us. But because one may have many feminine traits, that does not imply that he is a homosexual.

" A person who has no glandular or anatomical disturbance to cause a desire to wear feminine clothes, might have the urge as a result of trying to imitate the opposite sex. At one time or another, all of us imitate a person whom we greatly admire, either by dress or gesture. The eonist does so extremely! Havelock Ellis said that ' imitation in dress **can be a modified form of the desire for sexual union** '."—LORENZO J. CHIECO.

And again . . .

" Scientists believe that at the earliest instant of conception —the union of the paternal and maternal elements to form a new individual—the sex of a human being is decided. But it is also known that several weeks must pass before the determining characteristics have developed recognisable form. Some infants are born as one sex, so far as a physician's observation can determine; and, when they reach adolescence, it becomes medically certain that they have changed to the other. Furthermore, within the last few years, a few indisputable cases have been studied in which one person had the genital organs of both sexes.

" A person who has distinctively male organs, externally, can have the glands of a female internally and develop the secondary sex characteristics of a woman. The same paradox may be true in reverse. We see virile females shaped like men. In such cases, the psychology also is apt to be reversed ".—C. P. MASON.

4

THE STRANGE WORLD OF THE TWILIGHT PEOPLE

" That Sandra was one of the twilight people there was no doubt. To be having such a strange affaire with Julian, to have encouraged him from the start in his obsession—was not the work of a normal girl ".

So wrote Julian's brother in one of his many observations to Doctor Hermann Maxfield, of St. —— Hospital, Casablanca. He reported an attempt on Sandra's part to win him away from his unhealthy preoccupation with his brother and to recognise her (Sandra) as a woman. But so completely had she become identified, in Julian's brother's mind **with** Julian—he was completely unable to fulfil his urges as a man, and to follow up Sandra's assault upon his body and mind.

" Indeed ", (wrote Juilan's brother) " It soon became evident that I, also, shared something in common with the twilight people. For I was incapable of pursuing Sandra as another man might pursue her while, at the same time, I had an overwhelming jealousy for Julian, my brother, which seemed to grow worse and worse as the months went by. Yet I was never homosexually minded. Other men revolted me in that way. Even with the nymph-like boy-and-men associates of Julian—I was as cold as ice and completely unresponsive.

" With Sandra—after that first attempt on her part to seduce me (which I here describe in the following notes) I was as impotent as with other women. Yet I cannot pin any absolute sexual wish upon Julian or in any way confess that I had any physical desire for him. Even after his death—I was just the same. Horribly neutral towards the whole question of sex. I think possibly my mind was so overloaded with sexual phenomena in observing my brother, so non-plussed with the proximity of Sandra and her curiously bi-sexual outlook, and particularly her association with

Julian—that my mind refused to function along normal lines and, as a natural outcome—my body was ineffectual ".

Julian's brother followed up these notes with his observations on the attempt Sandra made to seduce him to her—and yet another account of a party for the twilight people to which he went with Julian . . .

" There were many more wild parties, on which Julian seemed to thrive ", recorded Julian's brother. " I went to many of them mainly to keep an eye on him, but also to further my studies in sexology.

" At many of the parties, Julian was the centre of attraction. And each time he returned to the flat, he was filled with exultation. His breasts had grown rounder, larger and firmer. Questioning him on this to discover whether he was taking unnecessary hormone tablets, he told me the development was due to his own stringent, daily massage. But I had my doubts about that. I had been aware for a long time that there was a certain amount of licence permitted Sandra, who still had her long sessions alone with him. So I asked her point blank.

" ' Yes ', she replied. ' Julian and I **do** have long love-making sessions together. I find it most exciting and most difficult to give up '.

" ' One day you will have to. Once he has had his operation '.

" She smiled at me. ' When that day arrives, we must get together ourselves. See if there is not something I can do to bring out the man in **you.** Because, basically, you **are** a man. Was it not for your obsession for Julian, I am sure you would lead a normal life, needing a person just like me as any normal man would. Even though I have Lesbian tendencies, as you know, I could still have a lot of desire for you '.

" She stood back and looked at me. ' You are good-looking, you know. You have a great deal of Julian's looks, but far more masculine, of course. You have a fine, slim figure '.

" A thought seemed to strike her. She looked at me with a quizzical smile on her lips.

" ' Undress ', she said suddenly. ' Undress in front of me. Let me be the very first female you have stood in front of, quite naked '.

" Can I be hypocritical enough to deny a thrill ran through me ? " wrote Julian's brother. " With cold, clinical detachment,

I reviewed the situation within seconds. As I did so, Sandra began to remove her clothes.

" To say she seduced me would be putting it mildly. Before we slipped to sleep, she surveyed my nakedness from tip to toe with admiring eyes.

" ' Were I fully for the man ', she said, ' I would be drunk with desire for you for all time. For there is nothing wrong with you. Nothing that a normal woman would not take to herself for ever. Your smooth, hairless chest and thighs, your waist so slim for a man, your masculine parts—what has been the matter with you all these long years ? '

" But to this question, I knew there was only one answer. Julian and my preoccupation with him.

" He came into the lounge the next morning. We awakened to find him gazing down at the two of us, lying side by side, quite naked, on the divan.

" We lay there, looking up at him. Aware of the tenseness of the situation but both, automatically, loth to spring up in confusion, to cover ourselves with the divan quilt.

" ' I hope you enjoyed my brother ', he said, smiling at Sandra.

" I got up, made my way to the bathroom, leaving them together. In this game of sexual wits—I knew I was no match for Julian.

" Here was I, a well known Harley Street Consultant, going to wild parties, being approached by kinky girls, having exotic intercourse with Sandra and, finally, harbouring jealous feelings for my brother.

" But what psychiatrist can understand human nature, and help it in its darkest conflicts—unless he has, himself, mixed in the half-world ? And, as a man, why should he not be tempted by those very things he seeks to cure in others ?

" So I sought to justify myself. And, in reading over my notes as I write them, I wonder how those who know me intimately will think of me ? But in my weaknesses lies my strength. I am cheered by the knowledge that, when I am not with Julian, dozens of people each month come and go in my rooms. And so many are cured in the long run. So many write me letters thanking me for having rescued them from the torments and conflicts that assail them day and night.

" Therefore I feel cleansed, from time to time.

" And Sandra ! She has opened my eyes at last. It is now a week since the night we spent together, and, though no doubt Sandra will never again approach me in the same manner, I know that there is hope for me. That she was, in a subtle way—telling me that it was hopeless with Julian.

" The terms of my father's will made it possible to realise more cash after a certain number of years had elapsed. This, together with some good investments I made from wise tips, allowed Julian and me to enjoy life to the full. My own fees from my practice were, of course, considerable, so Julian and I lived really well.

" Julian spent a great deal of money on clothes. His wardrobe was well-stocked with most all a girl could desire, with great accent, of course, on underwear. Every extravagant, sensual garment upon which he could lay his hands found its way into the flat. And he would spend long hours trying everything on in front of the six mirrors he had installed in his bedroom. In these, he could view himself from every angle, all at once, without moving.

5

THE MIND OF THE TRANSVESTITE

1

In Greek and Roman days, men wore short tunic skirts of various soft materials. These garments they wore as a matter of course. Roman and Greek soldiers, the manliest of men—great warriors, in fact—were dressed in this manner and there was not the slightest suggestion of femininity about them.

The women wore long garments that reached to the ground, completely hiding their figures and female charms.

And, when filmgoers of today see Greek and Roman Biblical epics on the screens of cinemas—they do not ridicule the sight of these men (stars and film extras) dressed in leather and metal breastplates and the swinging tunic skirts of cloth and silk of those days.

Man has been robbed of a great deal of his potential sex appeal because society and convention have covered his legs with trousers, demanded he wears a shirt and jacket, have thought up unsightly accessories such as braces and sock suspenders. It is a saving grace that, these days, dress designers for men's clothes go to town a little more in shirt fabrics and colours, design tight-fitting slacks and jeans for men.

Therefore, the young man and the older man who is not afraid of being ' with it ' can dress in such a fashion that he is able to exploit his sex appeal as much as possible. And this is quickly reacted to by females who demand that the men in their lives shall adopt such clothes.

There are, however, a great number of men who are not satisfied with these vague outlets—who are transvestites at heart and who are compelled to seek ways and means, in private, or with other men ' in the know ' or with sympathetic and understanding girl friends and wives, to find expression for their desires to ' cross-dress '.

The focal point of a man's or boy's wish to wear feminine clothing and female underwear is the burning desire to identify himself with females. There is a part of his mental make-up that makes him **dissatisfied with his male role.** As well—he may be possessed of a burning jealousy of the more elegant, appealing and more accessible role of the female and seek to emulate this.

The transvestite may find complete satisfaction in dressing himself in feminine finery in the privacy of his home and bedroom —and there it ends. Or he may have a desire to so dress and to display himself in front of other men dressed in this fashion. Or —he may like dressing up like this in front of girls—or he may like to display himself in front of unsuspecting girls at odd times in fields, from his bedroom, as part of an exhibitionist urge.

The thought behind this is, ' look—I am a girl just like you. Young, attractive, with a girl's figure, all her sex appeal. I am wearing her dresses or skirts and her underwear. Accept me **as a** girl. I am not a **male.** I am a female '.

Some men are fortunate enough to meet up with certain types of female who like to see men imitate **their** sex. Who encourage them in their fetish. There are hundreds and thousands of girls so minded—who get great delight out of buying their menfolk female underwear and other garments and watching them dressed up in them. Who make love to them in an inverted way when they are so dressed. Some of these girls marry these men and have a happy married life—indulging in a species of sexual intercourse that is more exciting and rewarding than the normal man-woman relationship.

But these girls are difficult to find.

Therefore, men with the transvestite mentality have to follow their obsession in private. This is more the case than with men who follow their liking for female attire by joining in with other men with the same tendencies. This is because, contrary to belief, the average cross-dresser is **not**—but emphatically **not**—homosexual.

There exists a greatly mistaken idea in the minds of the unknowledgeable and unversed and unsophisticated public that a transvestite **is a homosexual.** This is, many, many times, far from the case. The average cross-dresser hates the idea of men seeing him in female clothing and certainly shrinks from the idea of homosexual intercourse or love-play with other men.

And the reason is because the transvestite is dedicated to the

female whom he seeks to emulate and imitate. He **wants to be a woman.** But he wants to be accepted by **women** as a woman—and not by **men** as a woman.

That is the essential and the vital difference.

In Paris, man-into-woman shows are popular. The artistes—transvesti—as they are called—are accomplished performers and find a great outlet for their obsessions by performing night after night to audiences of men and women. The satisfaction they get from submerging their maleness at every performance and becoming—for the time being—'females'—is tremendous. It is a soul-saving escape from the maleness which they decry and despise. Women go to these shows to be amused—and come away fascinated.

The transvestite suffers from a desperate mental aberration that the average law of the average land will not permit to be paraded in public.

But, a girl can get away with any desire **she** may have to cross-dress. She may wear tight slacks and men's shirts, but no one will bat an eyelid. She need never be repressed or suppressed or inhibited. But—because the man is the aggressor in the sexual act —he may not appear in public dressed in any way other than the conventional male way.

The transvestite will find an outlet by wearing very tight jeans whenever he can, tightly belted so that his waist is shown to best advantage.

The mind of the dedicated transvestite is deeply steeped in femininity. He was born a male—but discounts, dispossesses and denies this fact. In his physical and mental make-up are the influences of a plethora of female genes. These project into his everyday life and cannot be denied. He is neither criminally-minded nor is he a pervert. He is a misfit in society—a society that, in England at any rate—seeks to deny his existence.

He is an onanist in that he pursues secret vice as an end-product of his sexual desires. He practises masturbation as a means of physical relief for his unfulfilled desires. But every time he achieves orgasm it is not from the male point of view. He identifies this orgasm with the female orgasm. Fancies—for a time—he is reaching the **female** climax.

And what is the simple, sum-total of all this ?

This man should have been born a girl.

Nature has played a dirty trick and invested him with male characteristics from a physical point of view but female characteristics from a mental point of view. Too many female genes affect his mental attitude. His brain has to condition itself to a **female mind in a male body.**

Is it little wonder that he seeks the soft silks and nylons, the frills and fripperies of the female. He likes music, the arts, literature. He is aesthetically-minded. How, then, can he reconcile these instincts with the roughness, the crudeness, the conventionality of the male?

The trans-sexualist is the desperate end-product of the transvestite. He is not content merely to dress up as a female. **He wants to be a female completely.**

He seeks hormone treatment to give him breasts, rounded hips, a slim waist. He wants to rid himself of body hair. Not to have to shave. Above all—he desires to rid his body—for all time—of the penis and testicles that give the lie every time—that pronounces to the world he is a **male.**

The ultimate operation for complete removal of the male sexual organs, called phallectomy, is the only answer to the extremist trans-sexualist. The only thing that will bring absolute peace of mind.

And how does it all begin? That will be explained later in the book, but here are some observations on how transvestites (cross-dressers) develop, from the pen of David O. Cauldwell, Sc.D., M.D., Editor of the book **Transvestism,** published by Sexology Corporation, New York . . .

" There are cases on record which throw much light on the making of transvestites. In one instance, a mother, purely as a matter of amusement, put a 6-month-old child into a silk stocking which was large enough to accommodate the baby up to the buttocks. She did this a number of times.

" The child evidently became conditioned to the feel of the silk against his bare body. Later on, the child was dressed in girls' clothes by the mother, who thought ' he looked so cute in girls' dresses '.

" In due time the young man became a transvestite. We have reason to believe that the silk stocking probably did as much mischief as the girls' dresses, because there is nothing stronger or more formative than early impressions on a child.

" We suspect that the fetishistic conditioning in this subject started long before he was eight years old.

" He may not even be aware of this. The point is that transvestites usually like the feel of silken things because they were conditioned to them early in one way or another. They may have been wrapped in a piece of silk cloth, or placed on a silk comforter, etc., or they may have come in contact with silk or similar cloths a great many times in circumstances which associated sexual excitation with the material, long before they could reason.

" Then, later on—as with this boy at the age of eight— the ' feeling of silk ' was remembered and a sexual experience followed ".

6

THE DOCTOR'S DIAGNOSIS

Doctor Hermann Maxfield, of St. —— Hospital, Casablanca, was about fifty. Grey haired, good looking, tall and infinitely likable. Sandra, as a private patient, had introduced him to many men and women desperately in need of help and advice. In the same way, indeed, that she sent many people to my consulting rooms for advice and medicine for the mind.

The doctor knew, of course, how Julian's course of hormone treatment had been so successful; and had been aware, for some time, that Julian would ultimately want to have the operation.

Julian's brother wrote : " ' But not yet ', the doctor told me. I learnt that, in Doctor Maxfield's opinion, Julian's physical and nervous system would need a few years of development before the very grave and very exacting operation could take place. Julian, I knew, would be terribly sad at this.

" ' The operation is forbidden in England ', said the doctor. ' Also, it is ruled out in France. The Roman Catholic Church abhors it. In fact, the Church of England, and, in fact, most denominations preach against it. A surgeon here or in France would be liable to criminal proceedings were he to carry out this operation in either of the two countries. The act of causing a physical man to no longer exist, though a woman might be created in his stead, lays open a practitioner to a technical charge of, well, shall we say manslaughter ?

" ' This operation, my dear fellow ', went on the doctor, ' is one of mutilation in the legal sense. It is not even castration for a definite and unavoidable and vitally necessary purpose. I agree that insanity could result from a state of mind and body similar to that which exists in Julian. And the law relaxes in many ways by permitting hormone treatment such as I gave to Julian. Further —were a man to try to commit suicide because he could not longer

79

stand the strain of his trans-sexual tendencies, an operation **could**
and **would** be performed in England, at any rate. Because a life
would be **saved.** You see my point ? '

" I nodded.

" ' And ', went on the doctor, ' so much of an ass is the law
that were a man to have a birth certificate that stated he was a
woman, it could be possible, after lengthy legislation and red tape,
for an operation to be permitted in order the man's legal status
could be reconciled to the facts on his birth certificate.

" ' But ', he continued, ' it is safe to assume that, because a
man is mistakenly described on the certificate as being a woman,
it does not necessarily follow he would **want** to be a woman, or that
the intense desire to change his sex would be influenced by a scrap
of paper, filled in and signed when he was too infantile to know the
difference **between** man and woman '.

" He looked through some papers on his desk and took down
a file from a cabinet by the door. ' The law and the medical world,
society and the church, acknowledge the existence of these cases,
but refuse, in concert, to pass any law that could automatically be
effective when occasion arose—other than the example of the
would-be suicide I have quoted you.

" ' In France ', he went on, ' a man may have, for a large fee,
his name changed from a male to a female one. But that is all.

" ' Julian's case,' said Doctor Maxfield, ' is about as genuine a
case as I have ever seen '.

" He looked through the file on his desk.

" ' I see that, at fourteen, his breasts began to develop more
than was normal for a male subject. His voice broke only to a very
slight degree and the nipples became surrounded by an areola—a
typical characteristic of the female sex.

" ' Then ', he went on, continuing to refer to the file before
him, ' actual feminine breast tissue began to form. And that ', he
said, ' was when Sandra brought him to me, as you know '.

" I nodded.

" ' Physically ', said the doctor, ' Julian could have been an
hermophrodite, due to modifications in the primary sex characteristics of the genitals. But, strange to say, his male characteristics
remained predominantly male, while his mental attitude became
increasingly feminine. The development of his suprarenal glands
which play a large part in the development of hermophroditism,

failed to follow through completely, with the result he displayed
feminine characteristics as far as the mammary (breast) glands are
concerned, but retained sexual organs of dominant masculinity.

"'Naturally, a confusion arose within him when he beheld
and cherished his feminine mammary developments but, at the
same time, saw, with feelings of dismay and disgust, his male
organs as developed as they should be for a boy of his age '.

"Again—a reference to the file before him before the doctor
continued :

"'The mind was then in conflict. And, since the feminine
mind was more powerful and more strongly developed than the
male, it became obvious to Julian that he should be a **woman.** He
began to disown his masculinity while, at the same time, having
to carry his burden with him.

"'There appeared to be no escape. That was why I decided
to give him hormone treatment and all the rest of the rigorous
routine that goes with it—in order to try to give him some sort of
peace of mind.

"'When his breasts developed properly, his facial hair disappeared and his legs and hips and waist began to grow obviously
feminine. His hair was allowed to grow long, as a woman's.
Naturally—a great feeling of satisfaction began to steal over him.
That, with the fact his voice retained its boyish treble with the
exception of a faint, attractive gruffness, made Julian feel far
happier. This, I think, was a great work of mercy '.

"'I can never thank you enough ', I said. 'Or Sandra for
having brought Julian **to** you '.

"The doctor smiled and waved away my remarks.

"'I could not bear to see such an attractive young person,
so intellligent and **aware** an individual, die the death of discontent ', he said. 'And I am delighted altogether with what has been
accomplished so far.

"'But ', he went on, 'we cannot afford to **kill** Julian. Either
mentally, because youth might ruin the success of the operation;
or **physically,** because he could not withstand the shock to his nervous system. A few more years will make all the difference to his
powers of resistance and endurance. Then—I have every hope that
Julian will eventually emerge from the hospital—a **woman** in every
sense of the word, other than an ability to bear children

"'Julian ', continued the doctor, 'is, as you well know, of

course, a victim to androgyny, a tendency of the body to appear to have female characteristics. His female breast development is a splendid example of gynaeomasty, as is also his lack of facial hair, his feminine pelvis and the general disposition of fatty deposits round his thighs. These tendencies were undoubtedly there —waiting to develop—from birth. The hormone treatment and the rest hastened development and magnified tendencies already in existence.

" ' His sudden transvestite desires, the wish for cross-dressing, were prompted by desire to see himself in the mirror as he **really wanted to be.** To present himself to the world as the **woman he thought and felt himself to be '.**

" The doctor closed the file.

" ' Little do we know, I think, even men such as ourselves, the tortures these people must endure. Imagine the man seeing a woman, beautifully dressed, having a perfect figure, exuding sex-appeal from every pore, moving sensually down a street or across a room. And desiring with all his heart, to be able to **look** the same, to **move** in the same way. To **think** in the same way.

" ' And he looks at the coarser clothes he has to wear as a man, longing for the softness, the texture, the brilliance of feminine underwear and outer garments.

" ' Can we imagine the dreadful jealousy that must exist as this man mixes with the beloved women of his choosing or sees them around him every day ? And what satisfaction can such a man find if the law and the State and the church refuses to do any-thing for him ? He can only retire to the privacy of his room and to the loneliness of his heart and there dress himself as a woman, and see, in his mirror, the reflection of his wishful thinking '.

" He offered me a cigarette and took one himself. We lit up and he continued :

" ' Then, sometimes, the desire to let the world know he is a woman becomes too great for him. He ventures into public places dressed as a woman. His mind is in a state of turmoil. He is tremendously excited. Trembling. He cannot think straight. He searches faces of passers-by for recognition. For acknowledg-ment that he is, indeed, a woman.

" ' But it is not as easy as all that. He is not clever enough. He is clumsy as he walks. His make-up is futile. His hips are those of a man and his clothes hang loosely on him.

" ' Possibly some passing homosexual hails him and he is at once appalled with the thought of what he is doing. Homosexuality is far from his desire. Nothing so bane or so crude. He wants only to be a **female.** Attractive. Desirable. **Woman** in the true sense of the word. More likely than not he is not activated by any sexual desires whatsoever. The woman he wants to be is, at the moment, sexless. Pure. Untouched and untouchable.

" ' He takes flight ', went on the doctor. ' Both from the man who has solicited him, and from his own fantasies so suddenly and crudely shattered. Back again in his room, he stares at the fantasy that confronts him in the mirror. Perhaps he strips and sees himself for what he really is, after all.

" ' A man.

" ' And he disowns this man he sees before him. But what way out is there ? Next time, perhaps, the police may get hold of him. Or some indignant woman will denounce him.

" ' There are more transvestite men in the world than society imagines. You see them walking slowly past women's lingerie shops. You see them buying women's underwear—surreptitiously for their wives or girl friends.

" ' And, as humanity fails—or refuses—to understand, in so many cases sexual desire is **not at the bottom of this compulsion.** This compulsion is as pure as that of the artist, the writer, the composer. Such a man wants to create an image and a likeness of that thing he loves most in the world—a **woman** '.

" He spread his hands out before him.

" ' Julian has triumphed. He has walked in the world as a woman. And why is woman-made-of-man so reviled ? Because she is an embarrassment to society. She is something they **cannot understand.** Yet they so easily understand the quirks, the kinks, the inversions and the perversions they enjoy in secret among themselves.

" ' **Every** man and woman has a secret sex urge—a deviation from the natural and the normal. And intellect and intelligence is sometimes born from perversion. Where is the truly great artist, composer, writer, who has not **some** dark part of the mind preoccupied with some other, more enjoyable, exciting and adventurous manifestation of the sex drive ? '

" He pointed to his filing cabinet.

" ' We both know ', he said, ' that in those files are names

of men and women in the public eye who are guilty of practically
all the aberrations of sexuality possible. Yet, all of them contribute
to the social scene, the arts and the crafts. Keep others employed.
Create entertainment and diversion for thousands of grateful
people.

"'Although procreation is the ultimate end of the sex urge, is
the **primary** reason for it, intelligence and intellect, the artistic and
creative and exploratory nature in man cannot and **will not** permit
of it to be a thing such as is used by the animal world in season.
Animals use sex to create their young because reason, intellect and
intelligence are not present to suggest deviations and experimentation. So well-doers will say, ' if that is an intelligent and an
intellectual approach to the sex problem—make me an animal any
time '.

"'But, of course', he continued, ' were we to be reduced to
the intellectual level of animals, the birth rate would become
entirely out of proportion to normal family needs and poverty and
disease would be rampant. Obviously, then, it is far better to allow
for experimentation than to allow sex to be used only for
procreation.

"'From that licence, though', he explained, ' it naturally
follows that deviations will arise. And there is a certain section
of humanity that hides behind prudery to condemn. In nine cases
out of ten—those who raise an outcry against sexual peculiarities
themselves suffer from some secret vice.

"'And', he went on, ' secret vice is about the worst possible
branch of perversion. It is selfish, precludes a partner, is narcissistic in conception and definitely harmful to the individual who
indulges in it '.

"'Is not Julian's outlook on sex secret ? ' I asked.

"'Not so', replied Doctor Maxfield. ' Because Julian's attitude embraces the world of the female. He does not seek sexual
satisfaction to the exclusion of all else. He has a goal to aim for.
He strives for physical perfection, the attainment of which will
bring pleasure to others. In that way—there is nothing **secret**
about his vice. Indeed—we dare not **call** it vice. We both know
Julian is suffering from a peculiarity of nature, and nothing that
has anything to do with nature has anything of vice within it.

"'In Casablanca', the doctor said, ' is a specialist for whom
I have the highest regard. And it is to him we will send Julian in

a year or two. I will leave it to you to break the news to your brother that it is not **yet** his time '.

" ' He will take it very badly '.

" The doctor shrugged. ' If he wants to live, if he wants the operation to be as successful as I feel sure it has every chance of being—he must have great patience. Before him stretches possibly a lifetime of happiness and contentment as a woman, with the stigma of man removed from him for ever. I can say, without the slightest hesitation, that he is an **ideal** subject for the operation '.

" I looked at Doctor Maxfield, whom I knew to have a very great reputation in the medical profession, and asked him why he was taking such a great interest in Julian's case.

" ' Because ', he said, ' I believe Julian to be a classic example of trans-sexuality, developed to a high degree. And because I think he will make a great case-history for medical records. Further —I am a compassionate man and I could see, as soon as I set eyes on Julian, that he was desperately unhappy as he was. Trying to struggle through to the other side. Not comprehending, in those early days, why life seemed so different to him and why he could not see it through the same eyes as those of his school companions and friends.

" ' And, let me tell you, ' he warned, ' I saw serious conquences if I did not begin giving him hormone treatment and helping him on his way. If Julian was still, to all outward appearances, a **man** in the strict sense of the word, there is no knowing what might not have happened to him by now. Prison, no doubt, for offences the law would like to call homosexual but which, of course, would have been the woman in Julian struggling for recognition. But you cannot tell that to a magistrate on a busy Bench. Or to a Judge in a criminal court. The law has little to no time for such things. Julian's life would have been ruined '.

" Looking at his files again, he said, ' Julian is a classic example of an individual in whom the action that impedes function of the normal glands was absent during the period of his mother's pregnancy. Also, the tissues of the gland of his opposite sex was present in considerable quantity at birth. Is there little wonder, then, that as adolescence approached—these things became obvious ? '

" He asked me to follow him into his library.

" Here, he took several books from the well-filled shelves. We thumbed through them together.

" ' Few people realise ', he said, ' how many cases of trans-sexuality history has recorded down the ages. And these are only a few examples brought to notice because the personalities were in the public eye. Goodness only knows how many cases are on record of which the public have no knowledge.

" ' Here, for example ', he said, ' is Catherine the Great, whose reign saw Sardan Paulus and Heliogabalus. And here is Henry III of France, and Phillipe if Orleans, the brother of Louis XIV.

" ' And here ', he pointed to yet another great name in one of the books, ' Here is Emil Auguste, Duke of Saxe-Gotha and Alten-burg. He was the great-grandfather of Edward VII. He was an author, poet and composer. Then we have the Chevalier d'Eon de Beaumont '.

" He returned the books to their respective shelves.

" ' Take Oscar Wilde ', he said ' as a classic example of the pervert who, had he been able to have his way, may not have committed the social sins he did commit to such a great extent, had society been more tolerant. Of course, he was not a trans-sexual in the accepted sense of the word. He was a homosexual without a doubt. However, had his glandular make-up veered just a little more to the feminine, undoubtedly he would have been one of history's greatest trans-sexualists.

" ' The lavender theme, as it is sometimes called ', he contin-ued, ' manifests itself in so many ways. But the greatest way of all is in the trans-sexualist, whose life many times becomes totally intolerable. And yet, the public will pay fabulous prices, in clubs all over the world, to be amused by pathetic creatures who use the tiny night-club stage to exhibit their frustration.

" ' Once ', he said, ' I saw an all-male show touring the music halls, consisting of a team of elegant young men dressed as women. They had a line of chorus ' girls '—they had their leading ' lady '. They were fabulous. Full houses every show. They were all tre-mendously happy leading their lives as women, before hundreds of people every night of their lives. The law was satisfied that they were providing entertainment. That nothing was obscene. But, had one of those elegant, feminised young men walked the streets in female clothing—he would have been arrested on sight '.

" He spread his hands eloquently. ' And there you have the
enigma of public opinion, the cramped ways of the law.

" ' Every transvestite or trans-sexual personality ', he went
on, ' craves an audience. And it is the function of this audience
to firmly convince the patient, as we **must** call him, that he **is,** in
fact, **a woman.** When that satisfaction has been established, the
patient is happy. And that sums up the total yearning of such an
individual.

" ' When the law relaxes, it does so to the extent it allows the
patient to be in a Home where he can continually dress as a woman
among the rest of the mixed bag of patients. But this dubs him
as a species of lunatic. And no unwilling victim to this aberration
is an idiot. The interests of the public who see more fortunate
victims parading before them in night-clubs are actuated by something **far more sinister** than the desire to have an evening's entertainment. It reflects the overall morbidity of human nature. It
shows that human nature—en masse—is **itself** perverted. More so
than ever is the viewer of trans-sexuality or transvestism. For the
patient's compulsion is healthy insomuch as he **thinks** and **feels** it
is the right direction, in which he should be travelling. But the
public goes to these shows merely to be sensually stimulated. And
the greater sin against society is committed by these people.

" ' Were Oscar Wilde ', said Doctor Maxfield ' to be with us
today, he would be the doyen of society. Féted in New York. A
riot in Paris. A sensation in London. His books would sell by the
thousand. His poems would be on everybody's bedside table.
Were, in fact, Julian to appear in night-clubs as he is at present,
he could command great fees—and the public would flock to see
him. But dare to change him into a woman via an operation, and
the law, the church and the State would be up in arms immediately.
Having accomplished the fact, however, somewhere other than
in England or on the Continent, he could return, with perfect
safety, and live his life as a woman. And that ', he concluded, ' is
precisely what we propose to let him do—eventually.

" ' Homosexuality ', went on the doctor, ' is one of the greatest tragedies of mankind. It is inverted living. It is one of man's
most pitiable illnesses of mind and body. All normal sexuality is,
first and foremost—psychic. Usually, one can find a history of
far-fetched sexual imagination and fantasy. New thrills and experiences dominate the homosexual life. The search for sensation

never ends. Reason becomes beyond control. The inverted **sex** drive is compelling. The victims search erotic literature for examples, such as I have given you, of great personalities down the ages who have suffered similarly. Justification is sought in works of art—whether they really **are** works of art or not.

" ' Normally ', said the doctor, ' the average man is bi-sexual. That is to say, as well you know, of course, that he can turn, if conditions and circumstances demand, to either of the sexes for sexual satisfaction and fulfilment. The same might easily be said of the woman who, many times, forsakes her husband for love of another woman.

" ' It is ridiculous to think that homosexuality is practised only by degenerates. That a low mental rating and extremes of poverty call forth these urges. It has been demonstrated down the ages, time and time again, that intelligence, intellect, creative and artistic talents, power, possession and position are far more likely to foster perversion.

" ' The lower classes go to the sensational night-club shows to get their sexual satisfaction. But the upper classes, with their more advanced and developed sensitivity and awareness of life, are more likely to turn into degenerates. Homosexuals and trans-vestites and trans-sexuals are not abnormal degenerates in the mental sense of the word. It takes brain and mind-power to follow-through an instinctive urge to an inverted way of life.

" ' Many people may be mistaken over Julian's case. His poor mother and father, no doubt, before their tragic end, may have considered Julian to be an out-and-out homosexual. But we know, of course, that **true** homosexuality can exist only when the acts of physical contact are the result of a homosexual attitude and out-look. Julian, we know for sure, has **no** homosexual desires in that he desires men as a man himself. Any possible sex life he may lead in the future when he becomes a woman will be directed towards **men**—but it will be with the wishes and the desires of a **woman**. Therefore, Julian will not be indulging in homosexual activities.

" ' I do hope ', said Doctor Maxfield, ' that I am not keeping you too long or boring you ? '

" ' Not in the least ', I said. ' It is good that we should have this discussion, for it clears up a lot of problems. Besides ', I

smiled, ' I am always ready to learn, and I certainly learn a great
deal from you '.

"He smiled and continued : ' Good. Well, my dear fellow,
it strikes me that a great change is necessary in social sanctions.
A thorough ovehaul, also, of social taboos is desirable. Years and
years ago, sexuality in most shapes and forms was regarded as a
departure from morality.   In short—sexual union was immoral.

" ' Our Victorian forebears covered the legs of tables and
chairs because they were symbols of sexuality. Articles of underwear were called ' unmentionables '.   Today, of course, modern
intelligence finds little connection between sexuality and morality.
Indeed, it is true to say that many people who are prudes, who
profess to complete or almost total sexual abstinence are, in fact,
guilty of immoral and amoral acts that are far more vicious than
are many sexual acts.

" ' Jealousy, deceit, malice, slander, libel, lying and cheating,
can be numbered among the sins of those who so control their
sex urges that they are made manifest in so many different
directions, the abstainer is more of a menace to society than if he
allowed himself to be natural. Or even—to engage in a vice or
two just for the fun of it.

" ' People who are abnormally sexually inclined, over-sexed,
given to experimentation, are more often than not, very high
minded, full of character and possess principles far transcending
those of the average prig, prude or priest.

" ' The church, I feel, has been greatly responsible for giving
sexual practices an impractical translation. They have aimed to
idealise sex. Science steps in and attempts to cancel out sex altogether as far as marriage is concerned, by introducing A.I.D. A
more sexless, unemotional, uninspired act than artificial insemina-
tion I cannot conceive.

" ' So many people, through the misguided influence of the
church, come to look upon sex as an evil. And, where cases such
as Julian's are concerned, a gross distortion of nature. And when ',
asked the doctor, ' is the church more required to be tolerant and
sympathetic as it is in dealing with a case such as Julian's ?

" ' But things are gradually improving ', he went on. ' Soci-
ologists, psychologists and medical men are beginning to educate
the public into accepting sex—and sexual deviations—as mental
illnesses that merit sane, sound treatment. The Wolfenden com-

mittee came very close to arranging that homosexual acts between consenting individuals—carried out in private—should be beyond the pale of the law. But the cautionary, civil-servant mentality of the law just evaded the issue. So it remains an offence, if discovered with sufficient evidence to justify police action.

" ' Man ', said the doctor, ' needs to eat, to preserve himself from danger and death as far as is humanly possible and—to satisfy his sexual urges—not necessarily or always as society, the church, the law and public opinion dictate, but in the way in which he finds ultimate and complete **fulfilment and satisfaction**. By that I do not mean he can rampage through life raping and committing assault, perverting small boys and schoolgirls. Marrying and having a dozen mistresses. But—should he suffer from a **real,** physical or mental sexual illness—then help should be at hand. Understanding and tolerance be meted out. So that a niche in life may be found for him. So that society may not be bothered with his difficulties because they will no longer be social difficulties.

" ' For years ', continued Doctor Maxfield, ' humanists and specialists such as Kraft-Ebbing, Schrenk-Notzing, M. Havelock Ellis, Magnus Hirschfield, Carl Westphal and Stekel struggled to bring more understanding to the masses in regard to sexual aberrations, perversions and inversions. Today, we see more articles in newspapers dealing with cases such as Julian's, more frank, outspoken books, more revealing situations on TV and more films that reveal the dark shadows of life to the general public. And that is an excellent sign '.

" ' Do you think ', I asked, ' that if Julian's operation is a complete success, it will become public property ? '

" ' This is difficult to say ', replied the doctor. ' The Press has an uncanny way of ferreting out these things, as you know. How do you think Julian would react to publicity of that sort ? '

" ' I think he might take kindly to it ', I replied. ' Julian certainly loves adulation. He could easily become a show personality '.

" ' And would you object to that ? '

" ' I would not mind, provided Julian did not cheapen himself '.

" ' He wouldn't be very likely to do that ', replied the doctor. ' Julian is an intellectual, I rather think. However ', he concluded, ' all that is in the future. For the present, you must tell him to come to see me and I will explain just why he can't yet have the operation '.

" And that was the beginning of the most troublesome period in Julian's life—apart, of course, from the time when he **had** his operation.

" That was his year of triumph ".

7

PRE-OPERATIONAL PLANS

" During the last few years before the operation, a great calm settled on Julian ", wrote his brother. " The wild party-going ceased. He made himself less glamourous in the flat, being content to slop around in tight jeans and shirts.

" He seemed to have retired into himself more than usual. I was aware of a certain embarrassment when he was with me that had not, in the past, existed. He was more careful, now, not to let me see him in the nude. His behaviour was altogether far more reserved.

" In spite of the apparent outward calm, it was obvious to me he was very tensed up. He draped all the mirrors in his bedroom and resolutely avoided looking at any other part of himself than his face in the remaining mirrors in the flat.

" On one occasion, however, he did unbend enough to show me a slim, white dress.

" ' This ', he said, ' is the dress I wish to wear when the operation is over and when I leave the Clinic and walk down the steps with you—a woman at long last and for ever '.

" I looked at the plain, almost severe, yet very appealing lines of the dress and nodded agreement.

" And, some days later, he brought before me a pair of men's black, tapered slacks, a man's white cotton shirt and a thin black sweater.

" ' These clothes ', he said, ' I want to wear when we go **into** the Clinic. These will be the last clothes I shall ever wear that will have anything to do with a man. And, when the operation is over, I want you to promise me you will burn them '.

" I promised I would do so.

" Between Sandra and me there was now a new feeling. Barriers had been broken down. She knew me and I knew her.

And, though no other attempt on the part of either of us was made to renew the strange magic of that first close association, there was an understanding we both felt made the long years we had known each other—so very worth while.

" With Julian also, she made no move other than to discuss the immediate future with him. He would sit and gaze at her as we talked of this and that and I could see he was enjoying every minute of her proximity—for he knew that very soon, if all went well, he would be like her . . . at last.

" One evening, Doctor Maxfield called to discuss details of the operation. He brought with him a small projector and screen. For over an hour he projected colour slides on to the screen, which illustrated, in minute detail, the operation Julian would have to undergo.

" All the time, he watched my brother closely, and I knew this was really a deep psychological move to determine whether Julian still had the moral stamina to go through with the operation.

" Watching Julian also in the gloom as we looked at the slides, I was happy to see no flinching away from the stark, cruel diagrams and actual, full-coloured photos that appeared on the screen.

" Julian sat, intent, watching each slide and listening to the doctor, just as if he had been describing an operation for tonsilitis.

" I marvelled at Julian's aplomb. Even I felt some repugnance at the altogether bloody mutilations I saw on the screen.

" Fascinated, though, Julian watched without a tremble on his lips.

" Patiently, picking his words with infinite care, Doctor Maxfield described the whole operation.

" ' Virtually, the man is turned **wholly and completely inside out** ', said the doctor.

(And so I remembered him saying when I re-lived the whole operation later—in Casablanca, during the dreadful hours when I knew it was taking place, and which I recorded so vividly in my mind as to be able to write them down for the sake of the record. They appear later in this book).

" ' The vital organ of man, the penis ', said the doctor, ' is dispensed with finally and irretrievably. With a firm incision and a masterly stroke of the surgeon's knife—the power-symbol of man, the fleshly stem of sinew and nerves, is severed for ever from the loins. And with it goes the potential for a million and one other lives. For the essential life-giving fluid will never flow again. That—in a split second—is the death of a man. The death of a million other men '.

" On the screen—the sad and sorry sight of dangling strands of flesh stripped from their anchorage. Forlorn and bloody, like a scarlet flower, they hung in disarray   .

" ' This is the point of no return ', said the doctor. ' Now—it is death—or the birth of a new personality.

" ' This ', he went on, in his soft, compelling voice, ' This is the act that incites the law to action. This is the mutilation the church abhors. This is the moment when man's mind can be saved from eternal destruction. This is the moment when sanity can be restored—when nature's misdirected work can be re-directed '.

" I saw Julian looking at the screen with fascination written all over his face.

" ' Those strands of flesh ', continued the doctor, ' are the streamers of skin that, for long years, have covered the penis. Now —they have been stripped away and the vital projector of the life-stream lies in a silver salver. Lifeless '.

" The picture on the screen changed to one of a raw, cylindrical mass of flesh, pathetic and strangely lonely, lying in an antiseptic, shining tray. And I marvelled at the miracle of this deft stroke that preserved the heart-beat, yet deprived man, for ever, of his ability to create new life.

" ' Then ', Doctor Maxfield was continuing, ' the scrotum containing the testicles is removed and, with it, the last vestige of masculinity '.

" He paused to change the slide.

" ' This is the moment of triumph for the trans-sexual personality, though he is, of course, mercifully unaware of it. The last symbol of manhood goes. What is left, at this stage, is an indeterminate wound—neither male nor female. Unproductive. Lifeless. Meaningless. Vital blood vessels are cut, joined up to others to continue, unchecked, the essential circulation of the blood stream.

" ' Speed here is important, as a haemorrhage is more than likely. The ureter, the tube which carries the urine from the kidney to the bladder, has to be instantly placed in a new position so as to preserve this life-giving function. The next stage in the hysterectomy is the forming of the ' vagina ', the ultimate process that imparts to the body the passive function of possession '.

" He turned to us and indicated the new slide he was throwing on to the screen.

" It showed a full view of the patient, testicles removed, strips of skin fanwise where once had been the penis. In the centre of this scarlet flower would be made the orifice that, ultimately, would be the ' vagina ' born, not of conception but of the surgeon's skill. A ' vagina ', however, that would never allow of the passage of male semen on its way to the womb, there to make and form a new life.

" For Julian, of course, would never have a child. There is no way—yet—of making a womb or of transferring the female ovaries and Fallopian tubes to the body of a man so that he functions completely as a woman and can become a mother.

" That, perhaps, is one of the tragedies of the trans-sexual personality. So many possess a deeply developed maternal instinct in harmony with their general feminine outlook. But this, of course, can never be realised or fulfilled.

" ' Before the orifice is made ', went on the doctor, turning once again to the screen, ' the continuation of the penis has to be removed. This organ extends back into the body quite deeply. This now has to be removed. This mass of muscle and nerves is gouged out, as it were, and the space left by its removal will ultimately be occupied with the ' vagina '. In some cases, artificial ' vaginas ' made of a plastic substance have to be inserted. This robs the new woman of a great deal of sensitivity in the sexual act.

" ' In Julian's case, we intend no such device. It is our great hope that we shall be able to provide him with a perfectly natural ' vagina ' made from his own flesh, carrying his own nerves and tissues so that, in intercourse in the future, he will be able to realise all the intimate sensations common to the normal woman '.

" Suddenly he turned the lights on and switched off the projector.

" ' That is as far as I mean to go ', he said. ' The rest of the operation will be described to you at the Clinic in Casablanca before you sign the final forms. So far—I have shown you what the half-way stages are.

" ' Well . . . ' he looked at Julian, ' Do you still wish to go through with it ? '

" Julian smiled and nodded.

" ' This is a **miracle** ', he said. ' And I shall have no hesitation '.

" Doctor Maxfield looked at me and shrugged.

" ' Then that is that ', he said. ' Before you leave, you will come to me for a final check-up. I, personally, am confident you are about the finest specimen possible on which to perform the operation. I have every reason to believe it will be triumphantly successful. That you will leave that Clinic a ravishing young woman.

" ' And this will show in your face even more than it does now. Softer, even more feminine lines will come to your features. There will be a new light in your eyes. Your carriage will grow even more feminine, for you will know that you carry the body of a female at last and that the irksome taint of masculinity has left you for ever '.

" A day or so later I saw some scrawled sheets of paper in Julian's handwriting, notes, it seemed for final inclusion in his Diary which he had so carefully been keeping for so many years.

" I could not resist the temptation to read them.

" ' Tonight ', I read, and saw the notes were dated the night of the talk with the doctor. ' Tonight I have seen, in vivid coloured photographs, the ecstasy that awaits me in the near future, when I shall become a woman.

" ' I saw a purple star that was the shattered remains of my manhood. And this was part of my body that would fold within me to form the most intimate part of a female. Whatever was the great joy I felt when my breasts grew and became rounded and soft and prominent, far greater will be my joy when I know that below my pelvis is that secret place that, in its tidiness, subtlety and cosiness, is the very focal point of man's desires '.

" Then followed a few rough drawings from memory, sketched as he had seen them on the screen.

" ' Bloody surgery this may be ', I read on, ' but a miracle. A triumph for the world of medicine. And what of the brain ? Suppose a man wished for the body of a woman—but still had the predominant mind of a man ? What could neuro-surgeons do for **him** ? Could they operate and put into his male mind the mind of a female ? No. This is something with which one is born. From the moment of conception—there is the mind of the female. Perhaps it comes from the mother who heartily desires a girl child. Perhaps it is a throw-back to many generations before. Perhaps it is because the father has failed in his masculine function and his seed has not been predominantly male enough.

" ' But I think it is a Divine Gift. What more wonderful thing is there than the mind and the body of a true woman? She is born to make new life within her. To feed this new life and to bring it up in the image and likeness of man. It is the projection of herself. What part a man plays in this is a very small part indeed. Compounded of pleasure and passion.

" ' Where is the man's triumph? Of what has he to be proud? Any fool can make a baby—but who can bear one?

" ' But of course ', he had written, ' I shall never be able to have a child. Even this miracle cannot produce that end. But the complete body of a woman will surely bless me with a strong maternal instinct—so that I may, one day, adopt a child as if it were my own '.

" This was a new slant on Julian. I had never been able to think of him wanting a child. In fact, I had never seen him evince the slightest interest in children. But these notes showed how his attitude was changing. And I marvelled at his courage.

" What I had seen of the operation from the coloured slides that evening convinced me that Julian was in for a terrible time. And I knew that, later, at the Clinic, we would both see further illustrations of other stages in the operation, and of the post-operative effects that would, to the layman, be most disturbing.

" Julian had already been warned that he would be in constant, nagging pain for many long weeks after the operation. Pain for which there were no known drugs.

" It was a true sign of Julian's innate womanhood that he viewed this prospect with stoicism. It is true that woman is blessed with a great capacity for suffering, far removed from that of a man.

" If this were not so—few children would be born.

" Doctor Maxfield told us the operation would cost us three million francs or more. We would have to pay a million francs in advance. Many documents would have to be signed, including my consent on behalf of my brother, Julian's consent and acceptance of possible consequences, were the operation to go wrong at any stage.

" Doctor Maxfield tried his best to make Julian change his mind.

" From a sense of duty and ethics, he felt he had to give my brother every chance in the world to decide, at the last moment, against sacrificing, for all time, his last vestige of manhood.

" But Julian would not be stirred from his decision.

" Then, after this episode, one day, into the doctor's surgery walked the Specialist himself, who was to perform the operation.

" He had flown from Casablanca to view his patient, to assess the potential of the case, and to get a first-hand analysis of Julian's mind and mental attitude.

" He was a tall, well-built, foreboding man without, it seemed, a trace of a sense of humour.

" Gruffly, he told Julian to undress completely. This Julian did in the presence of all of us. With cool, calm assurance. Without a trace of confusion.

" The Specialist looked at him from every angle. Various tests were carried out on Julian's body, humilating to the average man, but full of intrigue for Julian.

" Finally, he gave his verdict. He looked at Doctor Maxfield and nodded.

" ' As you say—a good specimen. Faultless. Almost unbelievable '. Then he turned to Julian again :

" ' Young man ', he said, ' Young man—you are strong and virile. You could make many babies. You could enjoy life as a man if you wished—in spite of the forced breasts, the womanish waist and hips and that luxuriant head of hair. You could, as a transvestite, make your fortune on the stage and in society. And still remain a full man. Tell me—why do you **want** to be a woman ? '

" Julian, standing by the doctor's desk, smiled at the Specialist.

" ' I was born a woman ', he said. ' But nature robbed me of her attributes and gave me the body of a man. I just want to rectify that mistake. I do not find it pleasant to live in a man's body. I wish to be released '.

" ' But surely ', demanded the Specialist ' Surely you have enjoyed the physical functions of a man ? You have been with women ? '

" Julian nodded. ' Yes, indeed. But, all the time, I have enjoyed just that extra ecstasy that women enjoy. And it has cancelled out that experienced by man. I am not a hunter by instinct'.

"'But you can satisfy that urge by homosexual practices', said the Specialist.

"Julian shook his head.

"'I can see you have very little insight into the situation', he said. 'And how could you?' he went on calmly. 'A homosexual satisfies the perversion of entering a member of his own sex, or by receiving a member of his own sex. That is a type of bestiality that has no spiritual or aesthetic value whatsoever'.

"He looked at the Specialist. 'To you, of course, the sexual function is a series of reflex actions on the part of the man or the woman. To me—sex transcends all other sensations and experiences. And the least of it is its physical significance.

"'The person, the place, the emotion behind the act, the nature of the act and the degree of emotional content and intent in the act are of far more importance.

"'A man can merely wish upon a woman the act of penetration, and it becomes an accomplished fact. A woman can desire to possess a man—and she possesses him. But a homosexual can wish upon his object of passion nothing other than passion, and that, in its most perverted sense.

"'I want a man to wish upon me the pleasure he can derive from treating me as a woman, and I wish to receive a man in the way a woman takes pleasure in giving herself to a man. There we have no homosexual instincts, just the normal man-woman relationship.

"'So you see', he concluded, 'why I cannot satisfy myself by homosexual practices'.

"The Specialist looked at the doctor and myself.

"'Then there is nothing more to be said. This boy has a vocation'.

"There followed an hour, almost, of signing forms in triplicate. Here, there and everywhere, had to be Julian's signature. And every time he signed his name, it was one step nearer the day when he would become 'Juliet'.

"He had to affirm no pressure had been brought to bear, that his decision was his own entirely, that both the doctor and the Specialist had tried to persuade him not to undergo the operation.

" That he, Julian, was of sound mind, aware of the great step he was prepared to take.

" He had to sign forms in advance, exonerating the doctor, the Specialist, the attendant doctors and nursing staff of the Clinic he had not yet met, from all and any blame attached to his decision and to disassociate them from any responsibility in the event of the operation being unsuccessful in any way—or of causing his death through heart failure, shock, haemorrhage, pneumonia, or any known or unknown symptom, disease, infection or condition that could result from the operation.

" He was handed still more forms in which he had to declare he understood and accepted permanent sterility, or the likelihood of frigidity. He had to declare that I, his brother, as his next of kin, would make no claims whatsoever against the Clinic or any individual whatsoever.

" When all this was completed, and the doctor and the Specialist had left, Julian and I discussed the matter.

" ' Worried ? ' I asked.

" ' Not in the least ', he replied. ' It's just the enormity of the thing that occupies my mind at the moment. I feel as if I were not really alive, but waiting to be born. Only I have the advantage of already being outside the womb—looking on. I really feel I have not been alive, after all, all these long years. It seems such a lifetime ago that I first started to look at myself in the mirror— and to wonder if there was perhaps not something wrong with me '.

" He poured himself another drink and continued :

" ' So many sexual perversions begin in school playgrounds and in secret places in long, age-old corridors. And the better the school, the higher-bred the pupils, the greater the vices. In those schools, one becomes aware of the fact that vice is the hobby of the rich. Strange that those in poor circumstances either have not the time for experimentation—or the intellect. I think, though, that unnatural sex is an outcome of too much good breeding, too much good blood, too much cash '.

" I could see a new sophistication in Julian. He had grown up tremendously in the past months. I began to wonder if perhaps he was not progressing too swiftly. That, in years to come, with his new life as a woman, he would not know too much. Know it all, in fact. There would be nothing fresh to discover.

" Would he grow stale and bored ? Would he lose his veneer

and polish ? His pose and repose ? How, in fact, **would** the long years ahead pan out for him ?

" This thought came to me suddenly as I watched him sitting there, the stem of a wine glass revolving between his long, sensitive fingers.

" What would happen when the years began to grow on him ? It was fine now, while he had his youth, his wonderful glamour and the exciting mystery that he projected.

" What of the late thirties ? The forties ? The fifties ?

" My blood ran cold for a moment. Would that bloom disappear ? Would he lose the firmness of his breasts ? Would that figure start to sag ? Would he, in fact, go the way of all women, eventually ? What would there be to prevent it ?

" And what of his mind ? How would he stand the strain ? What agonies of mind would he endure, seeing life slipping away from him ? His body growing old and uninviting ?

" Woman accepts this as inevitable. She conditions herself for decline and fall practically from the day she gets married. But did Julian hold, in his mind, an illusion of perpetual, feminine youth ?

" Looking at him as he sat there, I suddenly saw him as a faded, sagging, middle-aged woman, grey in his jet black hair, lines etched under the eyes and on the forehead. Nose-to-mouth line of discontent and disillusionment following the outline of tremulous lips.

" The grand illusion would be gone for ever.

" No longer desirable, indeterminate. Perhaps regretting, at long last, the loss of his manhood. Now more an object of pity, desired neither by man nor woman. Least of all—by himself.

" Man takes longer to age than does a woman. He retains the youthfulness of limb, the power and the potency of his sexual prowess far longer than does a woman. A man continues to hunt so long as his limbs remain active and his mind strong enough to direct the natural functions of his body.

" But woman begins to fade with the onset of responsibility. With the ebb of her sexual and reproductive powers. With the boredom and ennui and disappointments of married life. Julian would never experience all these womanly things, but no miracle on earth would preserve his body in a miraculous balm for ever.

" ' Why do you feel so strongly about perversion ? ' I asked.

" ' I think I hate homosexuality because I look at it from a woman's point of view ', said Julian.

" ' But lots of women are fascinated by male homosexuality ', I answered.

" ' I am speaking of the normal woman's aversion to it ', replied Julian.

" ' I do not hate Lesbianism ', he went on. ' I think there is far more excuse for Lesbianism than there is for sodomy '.

" ' Both prevent the normal conception and birth of children ', I said, ' And that is mainly why the law frowns upon it. Why do you condone Lesbianism ? '

" ' Because ', said Julian, ' the act of penetration by one man, of another, is unnatural. Organs are brought into play that are neither physically designed for such an act nor destined by Providence for such an act. But, between Lesbians, there is, in normal cases, no desecration of forbidden parts of the body. And great loves spring up between women as a result of such intimate contacts '.

" ' And between men also ', I remarked.

" ' That is a fleshly love ', said Julian. ' Born not of a wholesome, real desire for the passive partner, but motivated by experimentalism and a desire for the forbidden '.

" ' But Lesbianism is forbidden ', I said.

" Julian laughed. ' Not forbidden ', he said. ' Just frowned upon. Society tolerates Lesbianism because it has a more romantic air about it than male homosexuality. A woman, after all, is a frail, delicate, glamourous, sex-appealish person, perfumed and powdered. Made for love in any shape or form.

" ' A man, on the other hand, is invariably plain, probably ugly. Is powerful, unglamourous, unperfumed and lacking in sex appeal. The thought of two such creatures united in sexual union is altogether too much for the public's imagination. It immediately becomes revolting because man is the rougher, cruder and more forceful of the two sexes. But the thought of two attractive women indulging in Lesbian love-play is an altogether different picture to some people '.

" ' Except, of course ', I replied, ' when a husband finds his wife falling in love with a woman. That is an aspect of the eternal triangle he can't solve ! '

" ' Cases of that sort do occur ', said Julian. ' A man friend of mine has suffered just that situation '.

" ' And what were his reactions ? '

" ' Obviously ', replied Julian, ' to fall in love with the ' other woman ' and to take her away from the wife '.

" ' And did he succeed ? '

" ' He did. And now the wife has neither husband nor lover-woman ! '

" ' And the husband ? '

" ' He now lives with the Lesbian woman '.

" We then started to visualise plans for the flight to Casablanca, far off though this seemed to be at the moment. The time Julian and I would arrive at the Clinic, arrangements for keeping in touch over the progress of the operation and the long period afterwards, when Julian would be recovering and re-adapting to his new life.

" We arranged that Sandra would meet us at the airport on our return. Julian had wanted no one to see us off. Just he and I would make the journey to the airport. And there would be no one else until we touched down in England again, many months later ".

PART THREE

THE DAWN OF RESIGNATION

1

THE HIDDEN SEX

" Doctor Herman Maxfield presided over a meeting of specialists in gynaecology ", wrote Julian's brother, in one of the many-thousands-of-words-long dossiers he compiled during the years before Julian's operation. " My brother was present at this meeting, of course, as he was anxious to learn every single detail about his unique condition in order to fully prepare himself for the ordeal that lay ahead of him.

" The object of the gathering of specialists was to record Doctor Maxfield's observations on that branch of genetics dealing with the sex-change mechanism in the body.

" The doctor, after showing preliminary sketches and diagrams of the human system, dealt with the main points leading to hormone determination of the sex of a human being.

" ' The human body ', he said, ' is made up of 48 chromosomes —bodies bearing disinct colourings. It is this large group of chromosomes that determines—in the long run—the sex of the embryo child in the mother's womb.

" ' Out of the 48 chromosomes ', went on the doctor, ' two sex units are destined to shape and to form the sex of what will be, after birth, a new child. When a child is conceived, it is possible for it to be male or female. There is no immediate choice in the matter, neither is it possible for either of the parents to pick and choose for themselves nor, in any way, to be able to determine the sex of the child. No amount of wishful thinking on the part of the father or the mother will produce what one or the other wishes to have as a child.

" ' The female ducts called the Muller ducts and the male ducts known as Wolff ducts exist in the embryo child and, at that particular time and stage of the child's development, no one can say for certain what the sex of the child is going to be. At that stage, the child is definitely hermaphrodite—that is to say—it belongs to, or has the characteristics of, both male and female.

" ' It takes four months of development in the mother's womb before the hormones start to become balanced to the point where sex can be determined. The foetus will now no longer be of an hermaphrodite character. If the child is to be male, the female characteristics will fade away. If the child is to be a female, male characteristics will cease to develop.

" ' However ', he went on, ' this development of male properties or female properties in the foetus is never 100 per cent. on either side. That is to say—the male sexual factors do not always completely cancel out the female factors, and neither do the female sexual elements absolutely predominate over the male sexual elements. That means, in effect, that every child develops—to a certain degree—elements of both sexes, but either the male or the female becomes the more powerful of the two. And it is the more powerful of the two elements that stays the pace and produces the recognisable male or female child at the moment of birth '.

" The doctor paused to glance through his notes before going on.

" ' Unfortunately, though ', he continued, ' nature is not very fair over her distribution of sexual elements and plays tricks with the embryo child. In this way, and because of this uncontrollable and unpredictable game nature plays—no child is born with precisely the same distribution of sexual factors. No male child is born with the same amount of female sex characteristics, and no female child is born with the same amount of male factors in operation. So—a male child of one family will be born with a lot of the female in him. Another male child will be born to the same family with far less of the female factors, a female child will be born with considerable male factors in her, but her sister will be born with far less of the male in her.

" ' So these changes will be rung in families throughout the world—each child being male with more or less female factors, female with more or less male factors.

" ' Thousands are born and go through life without any

noticeable peculiarities, live happily as males or females, and go to their graves having lived blameless lives as good citizens.

" ' But some fall by the wayside—caught up in the vicious whirlpool of sexual indecision—both of mind and body. The predominating element is **body**, for **in** this unhappy body, are housed a plethora of sexual hormones that rule those hormones that give the outward appearance of male or female sex. The body then rules the mind. The mind, being the all-important and the all-powerful controlling influence in life—receives messages from the body and acts accordingly in the conscious life.

" ' The mind learns that all is not well with the body. Discontent and disillusion set in. A paradoxical situation arises in which the male mind struggles with the female physical element striving to get through—or, of course, vice-versa.

" ' Imbalance produces a moustache on a girl, an effeminate voice that does not fully break in a boy.

" ' There will, of course, be normal urges to lead normal sex lives with cases such as these. The girl with the preponderance of hair on the upper lip, the arms and the legs, will still have the normal sexual desires of the female. The boy with little to no facial or bodily hair and with a high-pitched voice will still desire women as a male should naturally desire his opposite sex.

" ' But, from time to time ', said the doctor, ' there arise cases where the preoccupation with the hidden sex, the deep-down-buried sex, holds greater sway, or where an equal proportion of male and female sex hormones swings in favour of the sex that is **not apparent in the physical body**—and the victim will mentally swing in favour of the desires and clamourings of the hidden sex. Will not, in fact, rest content nor be happy until and unless the desires of the hidden sex are satisfied.

" ' It is the constant, the drastic and the compelling urge to satisfy these deep-rooted desires that makes the patient, to all intents and purposes, anti-social, unacceptable and an outcast.

" ' The law and medical science allows a certain latitude in that they concede, in bad cases, the aberration, and permit the patient to be in hospital, there to satisfy the hidden urge by living as a woman if a man, as a man if a woman. The law allows re-registration in some cases, so that a man may be accepted as a woman, in order to preserve his sanity.

" ' Women, on the other hand, find it easy to live as men if they so wish, and if so their bodies dictate, and the law does not see. Or, if it does, it does not care. But a man must go through a great deal of trouble, be examined by doctors and magistrates, before he is permitted to have his birth certificate changed and is allowed to dress as a woman in public and to assume the female role in society.

" ' Rarely are these cases wholly and completely successful, however. While a woman can don trousers, cut her her hair short, look every inch a man if this is what her body demands and commands—and can take her place in a section of the community that will accept her in this way, the stricken male has to practise in private, wear women's clothes only in his home. This robs him of the ' audience ' he so earnestly desires—an audience that will look at him and **accept** him as a **woman**.

" ' And that is, mostly, the earnest wish of the transvestite, or the trans-sexualist. That his friends, his family—the whole world —will accept him as belonging to the sex **he** wishes to belong to, and not to the sex to which, to all intents and purposes, he **does** belong.

" ' That is the supreme tragedy of the transvestite and the trans-sexualist. The non-acceptance of society to see him **as he wishes to be seen.** Of course, this **is** a difficult problem to foist upon a community. Embarrassment, a crude sense of humour, morbid curiosity—all play their cruel parts in disclaiming a man-who-wants-to-be-a-woman-but-is-a-man.

" ' The average human mind is too attuned to a rational way of life, too conservative and too afraid of the unusual, to display sympathy or understanding. It is far easier to laugh than to be sympathetic. To deny rather than to acknowledge. To dismiss rather than to accept.

" ' Society is an ostrich. And it buries its face in the sands of convention '."

2

THE GAY LIFE

" Julian was an expert ballroom dancer, a natural outcome of his feminine make-up ", continued his brother's observations.

" We both went to many dances—he as my sister. On every occasion Julian was above suspicion and carried off the evening smoothly and with every confidence. There were awkward moments and episodes at all the functions when some fellow took a fancy to Julian and wanted the usual last dance and the drive home in a car. But these approaches Julian dealt with with dignity, neither rebuffing nor repulsing, and most of the would-be suitors were left with an impression of hard-to-get charm and delightful aloofness.

" Tennis was another of Julian's many accomplishments, and many gay games were played with friends during long, hot summer days. Julian always looked splendid in tennis kit, whether wearing white abbreviated shorts or a pleated tennis skirt and white shirt. He was agile and lithesome, winning far more games than ever he lost. We belonged to a local county tennis club and he was in great demand, playing regularly in yearly tennis tournaments.

" Altogether, Julian now led a gay social life, so different to the life of sordid parties of earlier days. He was now resigned to a wait of a few years before the decisive operation could be performed on him and seemed determined to get all he could from life in the meantime.

" It was practically impossible now for us both to go out together with Julian dressed in man's clothing. This would draw far more immediate attention to his condition than did his appearance in feminine clothing. Julian in tight slacks and shirt was altogether too female, with just that hint of male that gave the lie. So on all of our trips together, he dressed as a girl and there was never any trouble.

" On occasions, Julian would go out by himself dressed in a

108

smart suit or masculine casuals; but most of these trips were accompanied by embarrassments of some kind or another. Men would stare at him, girls would giggle after him and many a policeman would view him with suspicion. He was able to fix his long black hair so that it looked a masculine head of hair, but its extravagant length and luxuriant texture and sheen looked altogether out of place on a man.

"Julian would return from these lone adventures sometimes the worse for wear—annoyed, flushed and thoroughly out of temper.

"'Perhaps I should put a stop to this', he said on one occasion when he returned from a long, solitary walk through a wooded district near a week-end cottage we rented.

"'Some dreadful country yokel, red-faced and beefy, followed me for quite a mile and finally caught up with me. He was obviously a homosexual and he began to maul me about in a horrible manner. There was no doubt, though', added Julian, 'that he was convinced I was a **man.** Probably, had I been wearing my female rig— he would not have been in the least bit interested. There is something far more dignified', he went on, 'in the way in which a girl can put off the advances of a man than there is in the way a man can ward off the advances of a homosexual. I suppose', he said, 'it is because the mental and physical conflict between a man and a woman is a kind of game the whole world has learnt to play because it is a natural manifestation of life itself. Whereas the pursuit of a man by a man is unnatural and something dreamed up by man himself. The horror of seeing a red-faced, beefy fellow leering at one is beyond description. I know now so well how a girl must feel when she has any fellow—however nice-looking he may be—staring at her and trying to make advances to her. A normal man who had no homosexual tendencies would feel bad enough, but a person like me has to oppose such a thing not only with the revulsion of a non-homosexualist, but also with the naturally-repelled instinct of a girl'.

"Julian had developed a great capacity for enjoyment. We went regularly to the Proms—for he loved good music as much as I did. We visited the theatre, mostly musical shows, at which he expressed what seemed quite a jealous annoyance at the show-girls as they displayed their long limbs in many provocative costumes.

"All this time I knew Julian was still seeing Sandra with great regularity. There was no doubt at all about the great bond existing between them. As the months slipped by, Sandra grew even more beautiful. She never again made any emotional approach to me.

" With Julian, however, there was no doubt a strong bond. I always knew when they had been alone together, or out together, for Julian's face took on a new radiance and he walked and talked in a more feminine fashion than usual.

" One day, Julian was out with Sandra, dressed as a girl, and the gay life caught up with him. He and Sandra were sitting together in a copse through which a few week-end couples were passing, and the odd man or two, when two youngish men approached and sat down beside Julian and Sandra.

" It was quite obvious they were both out to get hold of a couple of girls and here, certainly were two, one dark, the other a red-head, who seemed ideal.

" Quite a deal of time went by, with the usual jokes and pleasantries, before the two young men started to try to kiss and embrace Sandra and Julian.

" Sandra got to her feet and pulled Julian with her. In so doing, Julian caught his foot in a rabbit hole and fell. He fell full length on the ground and his wide, short white skirt rucked up above his waist.

" The sight of white panties and suspenders was too much for the young man who was particularly taken with Julian. Forgetting himself, he attacked Julian and began to pull down his panties. To the horrified gaze of Sandra and the two men—Julian was revealed for a split second or so, as the man he was.

" An embarrassed silence followed, during which Julian pulled up his panties and struggled to his feet. Then the two men grasped the situation.

" ' He's a bloody man ! ' said the fellow who had attacked Julian. The two men at once turned to Sandra.

" ' Perhaps she's a man, too ', said Sandra's fellow. They set on her and, having discovered how truly female she was, walked quickly away, sheepish looks on their red faces.

" Julian and Sandra left the spot as quickly as possible.

" They told me ", records Julian's brother, " about the incident, and I advised them to forget it. But Julian, white-faced, was obviously very shaken by the episode.

"A few lays later, while we were in the cottage, extending our week-end into the week, a knock came at the door.

"Opening it, I found a man of about thirty outside.

"'I'm from the Daily —— ', he said, mentioning a well-known daily paper.

"I asked him what he wanted", wrote Julian's brother, "but the man pushed me aside and went into the small drawing room of the cottage.

"There sat Sandra and Julian together on the settee.

"The reporter took one look at them and said, 'Which one of you is the man?'

"'What the hell . . . ' I began, but the reporter cut in on me.

"'I know', he said, 'that one of these two girls is a man. It's been reported to me by a fellow in the village. He rang up my London office, and I've come down here for a story'.

"'There's no story for you here', I said.

"'Don't give me that', replied the reporter. He looked at Sandra and Julian again. 'The fellow said it was the dark one'. He looked closely at Julian.

"'You're dark', he said. 'So **you** must be the man dressed up in woman's clothes'. He turned to me.

"'Well?' he said. 'What about it? Is she a girl or is she a man?'

"'Get out!' I said.

"I seized him by the collar and pushed him towards the door. Sandra opened it wide and between the two of us, we got him outside.

"He looked back with a grin on his face. He opened his brief-case and took out a photograph.

"He threw it down at our feet.

"'Take a look at **that**!' he said. 'I took that yesterday afternoon. Didn't know I was following the three of you up Swithin's Hill—did you? I had had you all pointed out to me in the village by the two fellows who were with you'.

"He pointed to the picture at our feet.

"'Take a good look at that', he said. 'I am staying at the Green Hunter in the village if you like to see me some time this evening and tell me why I shouldn't publish that picture in to-morrow's edition—with a story'.

" As I bent down to pick up the picture he made off down the lane leading from our cottage to the village.

" Sandra and I took the photograph into the drawing room and looked at it with Julian.

" It was a large, glossy press photo, and showed Sandra, Julian and myself walking down Swithin's Hill. Sandra and Julian were hand in hand; I was a little way behind.

" Sandra's dress was flowing out behind her in the breeze. Julian's hair was fanned out round his head and his short black skirt revealed his long, bare legs. He had on a tight white sweater. A brilliant smile lit his features and he was half looking at Sandra.

" We sat down on the settee to look at it.

" ' This doesn't prove anything ', said Sandra, at length. ' It's just a very nice happy photograph of two girls and a man. If they published it with any suggestion that either of us was a man—it would be actionable '.

" ' But it **wouldn't** ', I said, ' because Julian **is** a man '.

" ' And that fellow who messed me about saw, with his own eyes ', added Julian. ' In fact—**both** of the fellows did. They would support any newspaper story that I am a man '.

" ' I shall have to go to that pub, the Green Hunter, and try to talk him out of it ', I said.

" ' I have a better idea ', Julian replied. ' Why not ring up the pub when we think that press fellow has returned, and invite him here this evening, and tell him to bring those two fellows who started the whole thing off ? '

" ' And then what ? ' I asked.

" Julian paused.

" ' Then tell them the truth ', he said.

" Sandra and I looked at him, amazed.

" ' Let the whole world know ? ' I asked.

" Julian nodded.

" And that was the way in which the case of Julian and Juliet first became public property ".

3

REVELATION

Julian's brother contacted the reporter, who was only too eager to come to the cottage with the other two men in question.

"Julian", wrote his brother "was quite keyed-up at the thought of the impending interview. Now—for the first time—I had a glimpse of the other side of Julian's nature. I saw the showman, the exhibitionist, the man craving for an audience. This was the facet in Julian's make-up that, somehow, made me think just that little less of him. It removed, temporarily, some of his ethereal quality.

"Sandra, though, seemed to bubble over with enthusiasm. She fussed around Julian, making him dress up in his most attractive casuals—a powder blue nylon shirt and a short, fully pleated black skirt. She spent a long time doing his hair in his bedroom in the cottage and examined his make-up with a more than critical eye.

"She dressed herself for the interview in scarlet jeans and a white shirt. I remained", continued Julian's brother, "in sober charcoal grey slacks and a sports shirt and jacket.

"Julian and Sandra came down the flight of rickety stairs into the drawing room—both looking radiant. Julian sat on the settee and crossed his slim, nylon-clad legs. His eyes sparkled. He looked on top of the world.

"We all three knew this evening marked a turning point in Julian's life. In fact—in the lives of all of us. For publicity in the national press could either be adverse and we would all be slated right, left and centre as perverts; or the thing could be so well handled that public sympathy and interest would be in Julian's favour and he could, almost overnight, become a national, a world-wide figure of intrigue, speculation and psychological and medical interest.

"The story could be made one great smutty joke, seen through

the embarrassed eyes of the fellow who had made advances to
Julian that afternoon, only to discover the object of his desires was
a man; or it could be a human story of one man's struggle against
the forces of Nature.

" Shortly before the reporter and his companions were due to
arrive, the phone rang, with a message from the reporter that the
meeting would be delayed for an hour, as the reporter had arranged
for the medical correspondent of his paper to attend the session,
together with a press photographer.

" This, of course, was the best possible news.

" It showed the reporter was aware of the significance of the
event and considered it important enough to get the medical correspondent on the job. Therefore, the write-up in the paper would,
no doubt, be authoritative and on serious lines.

" There had been similar stories in the press from time to time.
Quite a few sex-change cases had been spot-lighted in the papers
but, because of the unglamourous subjects of the sex-change, or the
incompleteness of the change from man into woman, these cases
had sunk quickly into oblivion.

" I felt ", continued Julian's brother, " that with Julian—
everything would be different. The fact that he was to undergo the
operation in Casablanca would keep public interest alive.   The
unlawfulness of the operation would, of course, be swallowed up
in the medical interest in the case, the deeply desirable and vitally
necessary psychological **need** for the operation in Julian's case and,
of course, the fact that it was to take place abroad and so be beyond
the pale of British jurisdiction.

" Exactly one hour after the phone call—they arrived. The
reporter, the two fellows, looking rather sheepish, a photographer
with all his gear and, lastly, the medical correspondent of the
paper. He was a doctor.

" After drinks all round, the interview began.

PRESS RELEASES ON OTHER FAMOUS CASES

When the interview was finished, the medical correspondent showed us a file he had brought with him that contained press cuttings from many cases of transvestism and trans-sexuality that had appeared in American newspapers—some of which had been paraphrased by L. H. Hamsley in the book 'TRANSVESTISM' (Wehman Brothers, New York).

After reading through them—we waited, with great interest, the outcome of *our* interview which, the medical correspondent said, would appear in the next Sunday's edition of '————'.

Here are the paraphrased extracts from the New York papers . . .

" In 1930, nine-year-old Freddy Sorenson was winning *considerable approval for the apt manner in which he appeared as a girl toedancer. Dressed in a short dance frock and with shoulder-length curls, the boy danced as gracefully as any real girl.*

" Not all of the masquerades end happily, however. In *Budapest during 1933, after thirty years, the sudden death of Mary Toth disclosed that ' she' was really a man. Even more tragic are the men who, tired of living a life of deception, seek release in death. Such was Frances Anderson. For thirty long years he had lived in the guise of a woman, and was known as the ' World's Champion Woman Billiardist'. Then, at the age of sixty he suddenly decided to end his impersonation. A razor finished the masquerade forever.*

" In 1936, seventy-six-year-old Charles Wilhelm donned *the finery he had worn as a female impersonator for fifty years, carefully placed a blonde wig over his own faded hair and hung himself. And in 1929 Mrs. Frances Peipper discovered the body of her sixteen-year-old son Arthur, fully clothed in her apparel, hanging in the kitchen.*

" Perhaps one of the longest of all impersonations was *that of ' Sarah' McPherson, who died at the age of fifty-one at Newburyport, Massachusetts, in 1925. Disappointed because the child was a boy, his mother dressed and treated him as a girl, naming him Sarah. Even when he reached manhood, she insisted upon his continuing the impersonation, and at length, after her death, he evidently decided that it was too late to attempt to end his masquerade. He was buried beside his mother dressed in the feminine apparel he had worn throughout his life, his graying tresses neatly coiled in a knot for the last time*".

4

THE FIRST PRESS RELEASE

" The interview was written up in a Sunday paper the following Sunday. Julian was offered a very good sum of money to give his name to the article and to allow his photograph to appear. An arrangement was made that, before, during and after the operation, the paper was to renew the series and was to have sole rights to publish, to the exclusion of any other newspapers, the full story of the operation and its aftermath.

" The article occupied a full page in the Sunday newspaper with banner headlines and three photographs of Julian—one as a young boy we found and gave to the reporter and medical correspondent, one of Julian as a young man in male clothing and one taken at the cottage during the interview of Julian as a girl, wearing the nylon shirt and pleated skirt.

" The headline ran :

" MEDICAL SCIENCE TO DEFEAT
NATURE'S TRICKS.

*Sex-change man attempts to triumph over
one-in-a-million body-mind condition* ".

" ' An amazing example of a man upon whom nature has played a strange trick was seen by our medical correspondent last week ', ran the lead-in to Julian's story.

" ' This man is Julian Griffiths, of ————, who, ever since childhood, has gradually been changing into a woman. In one year's time, Julian will undergo an operation to complete the change—to transform him from a man into a woman. It is accepted in medical circles that Julian Griffiths is an outstanding example of

116

a trans-sexual personality—a man born with the mental and physical characteristics of both a man and a woman '.

" Then followed a brief technical description of the medical and psychological significance of the state of mind and body of such a person.

" This was followed, in turn, by a short account of other famous cases in history of sex-change individuals. Then followed Julian's story, whipped up into readable journalese by the medical correspondent and the reporter.

" ' I look forward with keen anticipation ', ended the edited account, ' to the day when I can cast off for ever every vestige and trace of manhood and can be accepted by the world as a woman, and can at last belong to that sex for which Nature really intended me '. The history ran on for the full page.

" Back at the flat in Town the week following the appearance of the article, we were inundated with phone calls, visits from reporters from other newspapers and quite a few impressarios and theatrical agents eager to book Julian for night club appearances.

" Throughout—Julian conducted himself with dignity, but obviously enjoyed every single moment of this new-found excitement. Sandra, also, was fêted by the press boys and offered auditions by the managers of various night spots.

" I held myself aloof from all this excitement ", wrote Julian's brother. " There was something rather nauseating in the way in which the press and the people in show business were suddenly all out to capitalise on Julian's condition. He accepted no engagements, of course, but a gave a few interviews on the understanding that they did not encroach upon the preserves of the Sunday newspaper to whom he had sold sole rights.

" Julian's photographs as a boy, man and woman were syndicated throughout the world and appeared, that week, in the U.S.A. and on the Continent. In the space of a few days he became universally famous. Offers poured in from all parts of the world for cabaret and film contracts.

" Julian was no longer my property. Neither did he belong any more, completely to Sandra. ".

5

REPERCUSSIONS AT HARLEY STREET

" The press was quick to settle upon the fact that I was a Harley Street psychiatrist, and of course, I was completely unable to prevent them from making great play of that fact ", recorded Julian's brother at that time.

" News items in various papers the week following the Sunday on which Julian's article appeared were numerous. And this spread to New York where a certain well-known tabloid had this banner headline :

" ' HARLEY STREET TRICK-CYCLIST
HAS TRICK SISTER '.

" British papers were more sedate ", went on Julian's brother. " Naturally, I was asked to write an article in another Sunday paper as Julian's brother. I felt that, in the interests of medical and pathological science, and as an attempt to let the morbid public realise that Julian's case was of profound significance and not just a rather smutty joke, I **should** write an article. It appeared the following Sunday as well as did, of course, Julian's second feature in the other Sunday paper ".

(The following extracts were reproduced in a B.M.A. House Journal and in a medical publication in the U.S.A.)

" . . . imagine for a moment ", wrote Julian's brother, " the psychological re-adjustment necessary to a human being who has lived life as a male (in spite of intense female desires) and who has suddenly to completely change and re-mould his entire mental outlook to that of a female. That will be just **one** of my brother's tasks if and when he has successfully recovered from the sex-change operation.

" A whole new philosophy will have to be formulated. A new

set of principles, a new code of morals. Indeed—an entirely new concept of life from a religious point of view as well. This is not merely a matter of realising a sensual dream. It is a powerfully compelling urge to be entirely re-born, to go through the pangs of birth, as it were, all over again. But, this time, it is not the mother but the ' child ' who will suffer the pangs of this mysterious ' re-birth '.

" How little can the layman know of such things ? To him, this is just an embarrassment—a freakish trick of nature . . . perhaps, even, a little repugnant. But this is a mistake of conception as much as is the infant born with a malformation of the body or with a mentally defective mind.

" . . . psychosomatic medicine teaches the relationship between mind and body. The mind dictates—and, as it dictates—so does the body **react.** The mind tells the body there will be pain, and there **is** pain. The mind tells the body to sweat with fright, to shake with glee, to sob with happiness, to jump for joy, to cry, to laugh, to run, jump, walk. In just the same way the mind can tell the male body it is **feminine,** the mind can tell the female body it is **male.** Looking down at the male or female body—whatever **thoughts** try to give it the lie—nothing will alter the indisputable structure, be it male or female.

" But—and this is the all-important proviso—if mental attitude is so powerful and so dominating as to amount to a compulsion and, later, to a neurosis, the influence of auto-suggestion can be so great as to convince the body that it does, in fact, belong to the opposite sex to that to which it appears to belong physically.

" Movements of the body, guided and dictated by the all-powerful mind, then begin to assume the appearance of the desired sex. And this, apart from any changes brought about by hormone treatments. The man becomes effeminate in walk, mannerisms, affectations. Public opinion seeks to make fun of this. But they behold one of the unique tragedies common to men, and one of the unhappiest of dilemmas—made more unfortunate by society's attitude and the short-sighted arm of the law.

" Psychomatically controlled—the transvestite or the trans-sexualist plays a role to which he feels he is most suited— that of a woman. The aesthetic things in life he appreciates more than does the mere male, more, in fact, than does the one-hundred-per-cent. female. For, in his role, all things female are exagger-

ated.   He is more conscious of being female than is a female
herself. He is more conscious of his body—to which, sometimes,
the average female gives little thought.

" He is more concerned with his looks because, forever, he
has to be sure he appears well and truly feminine. The inherent
male within must never be allowed to protrude or intrude. His
voice must be well-modulated, so that any male gruffness is dispensed with.   His behaviour and his manners have to undergo
drastic revision. It is not **he** who now stands when a female enters
a room. He remains seated.   It is to **him** to whom all the little
masculine chivalries and courtesies are now directed. **He** has the
proffered seat in the full railway compartment. It is to **him** doors
are opened, wines and foods are offered.

" When the operation for removal of the male genitals has
successfully been performed the trans-sexualist subject will have
to adapt himself finally to his new part in life. But he has also to
be careful not to overplay his new part. His delight in finding himself well and truly female may, at first, go to his head. He may
begin to exaggerate every movement, be over-voluptuous, ever-
anxious not to appear in the least bit male.

" To those who know the true facts of the case—that he is a
trans-sexual who has had the ultimate operation—he may appear
absurd and they may get the impression he is not entirely feminine.
To those who do **not** know the true facts of the case—he may
appear either as an eccentric, coquettish girl with nymphomaniac
tendencies, or he may be taken to be an unsuccessful transvestite
who cannot quite make the grade.

" The weeks and months following the operation are, therefore, fraught with trial and error. It must always be remembered
that, deep down in the trans-sexual's mind, is the knowledge that
he is, **really and truly**—masculine.

" Here is an artificial vagina, here are hormone-induced
breasts. And—so very importantly—here is a masculine subconscious mind that—for many years before the change began and
was completed—thought masculine thoughts, and stored these
thoughts as all thoughts **are** stored by the subconscious.

" From time to time, in sudden crises—these impressions,
buried deep, are brought to the surface, sometimes through the
complex action of association of ideas. If and when such a crisis
does arise—how will he react ?

" Will his conscious mind come to the rescue in time, to remind him he is a ' woman ' and that—as such—certain subconscious reactions would be unwomanly ?

" In the heat of the moment, would this new ' woman ' lash out with his fists as would the now-buried man ?

" Would ' she ' give way to abusive or obscene language ?

" Would ' she ' go to the rescue of a genuine woman in distress —as befits the normal man ?

" Would ' she '—in effect—revert to type ?

" A great deal depends on the sort of life the trans-sexual subject leads after the operation. Is it to be a public life or a private life ?   This will depend to a great extent on the success of the operation and the outlook of the subject. If the trans-sexual personality has latent gifts for dancing, singing or acting, is an able study for a theatrical manager who can see good show business potential—then he may well make a great success of a public life until of such an age when he is no longer a public curio and his looks begin to fade.

" If, however, the subject has no special gifts in these directions and it is quite obvious no such talents could be cultivated—the trans-sexual personality would lead an ordinary, private life among friends and relatives.

" But what of the extremely dangerous situation that could arise were the trans-sexual subject to fall in love with a man ?

" That is as real a problem as can be imagined.

" Such a person is fully capable of experiencing, and of wishing to experience, the full range of human emotions. In this case —not as a man, but as a woman.   But bear in mind that this ' woman ', while being capable, as far as her new body will allow, of making love and being made love to as a **woman**—' she ' also knows and fully understands the mechanics of the **male love technique.**

" Years before the operation, it is more than likely that the masculine strain has demanded an emotional and sexual life as a man and that this has been fulfilled. The new ' woman ', therefore, would approach the question of love-making with two minds—that of a man and that of a woman.

" Which mind would predominate at the crucial moment ?

" It can be assumed that, since the dominant preoccupation of the subject has been to become a woman—then the feminine instincts in lovemaking will come to the fore. And that, robbed off the masculine member—there would be no question at all of what particular role the subject **would** play physically.

" But the all-important question of **mental** attitude—deeply buried in the male subconscious, cannot be ruled out. Would the trans-sexual subject be content to play the passive role always ? Would not the dormant, masculine ' hunter ' and active instinct wish to assert itself from time to time ?

" How would this affect the **real** man of the union—the husband ?

" Assuming the husband knew the full facts of the case, was not being misled into thinking he was marrying a genuine woman, and was prepared for all that might befall such a union—would he not have to be very versatile, very human and very understand-ing—to accept such a situation ? Perhaps, sometimes, to allow his partner full reign for the masculine promptings ?

" Suppose, also, the maternal instincts of the new ' woman ' became suddenly very strong, as well they might, for ' she ' would, undoubtedly, have **some** maternal instincts as part of the intricate and deep-rooted desires to **be** a woman ? This new ' woman ' could never, of course, bear a child, for no operation on earth will construct Fallopian tubes, ovaries and a womb inside the body of a man, whatever miracles may be performed with the sexual organs. So there arises a thwarted maternal instinct that can never be satisfied through the normal channels.

" Adoption ? It is extremely unlikely that the adoption laws of any country would see eye-to-eye with a trans-sexual subject becoming a foster mother or agree to hold the husband fully res-ponsible for, or fully in command of, such a situation. There would seem to be, therefore, little to no solution to that particular situation.

" These factors are brought to notice in order to illustrate what a very serious step emotionally, physically and spiritually is taken by a subject who asks for, and is granted, the privilege of a phalloctomy.

" Curious and morbid members of the public, unaware of the intricacies of such a situation, are apt to gloss over the deeper, more serious and more significant facts of such a situation.

" Here is real tragedy.

" Here is a situation as real as is any cancer of the body or aberration of the mind.

" Certain hospitals have, as inmates, men who have never, and **will** never, undergo the operation that will make them apparently feminine. They will never even have hormone treatment that will help them to look even remotely feminine.

" So they have to go through life, in homes and in hospitals throughout the world, being permitted to dress as women, to behave as women and to be treated as women by the staff and those of the inmates with whom they are surrounded who are willing to act out the charade.

" They live a mental life as a woman, but, when they survey their bodies in a mirror, they see the true man reflected back at them.

" Some magistrates and doctors have it in their power to grant a new birth certificate to such men which permits them to be re-registered as ' women ' and to take a certain place in society **as** ' women ' and not to have to spend most of their lives as inmates of homes and hospitals.

" But such cases are rare. The most prevalent state is that of the man who hugs this aberration to himself. Who lives a secret life of a woman in his mind, finding expression for his fantasies only in secret. Sharing it with no one but his own private mirror.

" This is the saddest part of the problem.

" He cannot share his secret with his friends, his family, with his girl friend if he has one, or with his wife if he is married.

" He is not homosexual by nature, for few, if any, true transvestites and trans-sexualists **are** homosexually inclined. Therefore he does not share his secret with other men. But there **are** rare cases where a man so inclined meets another man, or group of men, suffering from the same misfortune, and these men get together, from time to time, and enjoy their secret among themselves.

" There are, also, men who are lucky enough to meet understanding girls and women who are willing to indulge them in their whims and fancies. But such females are, naturally, hard to find.

" In the U.S.A., transvestism and trans-sexuality finds an outlet in clubs for such people. It is not frowned upon quite so much as it is in Great Britain. On the Continent, too, more freedom is allowed for expression of this particular male fantasy.

" It should be grasped that transvestism and trans-sexuality is a disease of mind and body. A genuine misfortune. A harmless but anti-social quirk of human nature. Its main menace is that it is a source of embarrassment to society.

" British newspapers report, from time to time, cases of men appearing in the dock wearing the female clothing in which they have been arrested in the street. Such men deserve to be treated with sympathy and full understanding. Their's is no crime provided they have not been soliciting men for immoral purposes in a public place.

" Even so—the law needs to get deep down inside the fantasy-ridden minds of these unfortunate men. To try to understand how their lives are one horrible nightmare. How they live with the conviction they **should be women** but are men.

" It should be made perfectly clear to the public, the law, to the church and to the State that there is an essential difference between the confirmed and practising homosexual and the trans-vestite and trans-sexual personality.

" The homosexualist practises an unnatural vice. The trans-vestite or trans-sexualist seldom practises **any** vice.

" His only sin is that he wishes to be a woman ! "

6

SPECIALIST OPINIONS

"Transvestism and trans-sexuality have fascinated and intrigued medical men and psychiatrists for many long years", wrote Julian's brother.

"In the archives of the Clinic at Casablanca are the recorded opinions of many famous specialists in the fields of abnormal psychology and gynaecology. I was considerably honoured to be told that my own particular observations on the subject were also to be filed for future reference in guiding doctors and psychologists in cases of these types.

"I spent many long hours in the libraries of the Clinic and Hospital reading through many thousands of words on the subjects and found it most interesting to note the various interpretations well-known specialists put on the two states of mind that constituted the transvestite and trans-sexualist urges.

"Among the few that I found quite notable were the opinions of Winfield Scott Pugh, B.S. M.D., Harry Benjamin, M.D., the well-known British psychologist and Nature-Cure specialist, Mark Tarail, B.A., M.S., and David O. Cauldwell, Sc.D., M.D.

"Extracts from their opinions, reproduced from 'Transvestism', edited by David O. Cauldwell, published by Sexology Corporation, New York, and Wehman Bros., Publishers, of 712 Broadway, N.Y.3, are given here:"

Types of Transvestites

These males are of several types:

(1) The **heterosexual**—loving the opposite sex, in the natural way;

(2) The **bisexual,** with an attraction both to virile masculine women and to feminine men;

(3) The **homosexual**—loving only his own sex;

(4) The **narcissistic** or **self-loving** (very common), in which the feminine components of the subject's own personality give complete satisfaction to his masculine elements;

(5) The **assexual** or **psychologically sexless** variety, often impotent and finding full satisfaction in some feminine occupation, like that of a domestic servant.

There is not the slightest doubt that all of these types exist, as it has been my own privilege to observe them. A well-known scientist tells us he divides the transvestites into other groups, as follows :

(A) Men adopting women's garb;

(B) Women adopting male clothing;

(C) Adults returning to the raiment of childhood.

Another eminent physician insists that transvestism is really a concealed form of homosexuality. This opinion is doubted by others, because many of these cases never reach anything suggesting the true homosexual stage.

There is an important point many observers seem to have overlooked and that is : we are all products of a male and female. Therefore, it is no wonder to me to find evidence of femininity in a male body and traces of the masculine in our fair sex. It is indeed most surprising that we do not see more of these transvestites; however, there are, no doubt, many whose secrets remain closely guarded—*Winfield Scott Pugh, B.S., M.D.*

Relation to Homosexuality

In transvestism the sex organs are sources of satisfaction; in trans-sexualism they are sources of disgust. This is an important distinction and perhaps the principal difference. Otherwise there is no sharp separation between the two, one merging into the other. It is quite evident that under the influence of sensational publicity, a reasonably well-adjusted transvestite could become greatly disturbed and fascinated by ideas of surgical conversion.

Homosexual inclinations always exist in the trans-sexualist, whether they result in actual physical contacts or not. The libido (sexual desire) as far as sex activities are concerned is usually low and seems to be completely occupied with the sex conversion idea, indicating the close relationship to **narcissism** (love of one's self). The interpretation of the libido as **homosexual** is strongly rejected

by the male trans-sexualists. They consider the fact that they are
attracted to men naturally, **because they feel like women** and consider themselves of the female sex.

Transvestites, on the other hand, are mostly **heterosexual,**
although their principal sexual outlet seems to be **auto-erotic.** Some
are married and raise families, but the marriage rarely endures.
Others have understanding girl friends with whom they sometimes
share their wardrobe.

Alfred C. Kinsey and his associates consider transvestism and
homosexuality " totally independent phenomena ". So they are, as
far as overt behaviour is concerned. Most homosexuals would not
be interested in " cross-dressing ", just as most transvestites reject
homosexual relations—*Harry Benjamin, M.D.*

Conditioned Inclination

One of the most thorough-going studies of human sexual behaviour in males and females was made by Dr. Alfred C. Kinsey
and his associates in the Institute for Sex Research at the University
of Indiana. Dr. Kinsey's investigations have led him to consider
transvestism as a distinct anomaly separate from homosexuality.
Together with many other psychiatrists and psychologists, he believes that this sexual deviation is a psychologically conditioned
inclination acquired after birth as a result of precise and specific
environmental experiences. He disputes the theories of glandular
causation and constitutional origin.

" Psychologically ", says Dr. Kinsey, " the phenomenon (of
transvestism) sometimes depends upon an individual's erotic
attraction for the opposite sex. A male, for instance, may be so
attracted to females that he wishes to be permanently identified
with them. He wants to have sexual relationships with them, and
he wishes to live permanently with them, as another female might
live with them. The neighbours may believe it to be two females
who are living together, although it is sexually a heterosexual relationship which is involved.

" Sometimes transvestism depends upon an individual's
violent reactions against his or her own sex. If he is attracted, he
may have heterosexual relationships. But he may so idealise females that he is offended by the idea of having sexual relationships
with them, and then he may be left without any opportunity for

socio-sexual contacts, because his dislike for individuals of his own sex will prevent him from having sexual relationships with them.

" There are some psychiatrists who consider all transvestism homosexual, but this is incorrect. Transvestism and homosexuality are totally independent phenomena, and it is only a small portion of the transvestites who are homosexual in their physical relationships . . . "—*Mark Tarail, B.A., M.S.*

Amateur Theatricals

Transvestism does not necessarily involve homosexuality. **Few transvestites are homosexuals.** It is interesting, however, to note that various affairs, such as stage masquerades and amateur plays in which a certain number of males impersonate females, are arranged by male homosexuals. The writer knows this because he has personally received numerous letters in which male homosexuals explained their reasons for promoting such affairs. It gave them an opportunity to see males disrobed.

On various occasions, newspapers have published pictures of the characters in amateur plays. It is not difficult when looking at these pictures, to identify the actual transvestites. Although one knows that none of the characters are women, those individuals who are correctly dressed in female attire and who look like women are real transvestites, while those less meticulously groomed have either been " roped in " or have taken part because of a mild interest in cross-dressing.

Some transvestites are so clever in their practices that they dress and live for years as members of the sex to which they do not belong. Many such cases, when discovered through some inadvertency on their part, have been publicised in the press. Although he has no tabulation, it is the writer's impression that these instances have more often involved females. The sex of numerous of such individuals has been revealed through illness, sometimes crime and death.

Interesting is that phase of transvestism wherein wives insist that their husbands dress as women. It seems likely that in some of these cases the wife has a strong inclination towards **lesbianism** (female homosexuality). In a few instances, the writer has received letters from husbands stating that their wives had admitted " early " homosexual experiences.

Instances have occurred involving two female homosexuals

who actually got married. This involved the necessity for one of them to cross-dress. Now and then such a case is discovered and details are given in the Press. In one such instance, although the marital plan did not materialise, the more masculine of the two girls planned to dress as a man, work and make the living, and " grow a moustache ". In a fit of jealousy, the female husband-to-be murdered her bride-to-be by slashing her throat.

—*David O. Cauldwell, Sc.D., M.D.*

7

JULIAN'S WORD-ASSOCIATION TEST

"One of the most interesting and revealing of psychological tests is that known as the word-association test, in which words are shot at the patient at considerable speed and he is required to answer each word immediately with a word of his own that is, at once, conjured up by the association of the word the psychologist uses". *(This word-association test was included in Julian's brother's papers on the case, and is reproduced here to show Julian's remarkable and immediate reactions—and to demonstrate the extremely strong pre-possession he had with femininity and all that it meant to and for him).*

"Julian", wrote his brother, "underwent the word-association test shortly after the series of articles supposed to be written by him started to appear in the Sunday papers. Although of course, Julian supplied the correct data and correct facts to the Sunday newspaper, the journalists in charge of the features rewrote them and turned them into excellent and sensational journalism.

"It was obvious that, with the sudden publicity accorded him —a whole new and exciting life was opening up for Julian. Since it meant further promotion for the projected image of himself as a girl, naturally Julian took all that came along before his operation. In fact—he accepted an offer to appear in a night club. *(This account of Julian in a London night club was edited by research workers at the Clinic and extracts appear in the next chapter).*

"The word-association test was carried out by Doctor ——, a specialist in neurology in London, with connections with the Casablanca Clinic.

"Eder's famous test—the one hundred Free Association Test Words—was used to examine Julian's reactions. Although the examiner was well satisfied that Julian was a fully-fledged transsexualist and transvestite, he deemed it an interesting and necessary
130

test of the depths of Julian's subconscious in order to discover just how deeply Julian's feminine convictions went.

"Here are the test words as uttered by Doctor ——, and next to them are the response-words spoken by Julian.

"It will be seen how the predominating theme of each response-word has a feminine connection in Julian's case. For instance—an ordinary patient, responding to the word-association test might respond in this way :

Psychologist's word	Patient's word
head	shoulders
green	grass
water	sea

"Such word-reactions illustrate a perfectly natural and normal response either to the opposite of the word spoken by the specialist or a word that the first word conjures up, and which is a perfectly acceptable follow-up word.

"In Julian's case, few, if any, of **his** response-words would be expected of a normal man, but were response-words anticipated to be uttered by a man who was suffering from the particular mental and physical afflictions with which Julian was affected.

Doctor	Julian
head	body
green	jealousy
water	chamber
sing	love song
dead	angel
long	penetrate
ship	she
make	love
woman	girl
friendly	make love
bake	cake
ask	for love
cold	naked
stalk	possess
dance	frock
village	love
pond	reflection
sick	nurse
pride	beauty

Doctor	*Julian*
bring	carry
ink	love-letter
angry	whip
needle	thrust
blue	baby
lamp	red
carry	baby
bread	wife
rich	clothes
tree	lover
jump	night
pity	love
yellow	jealousy
street	walker
bury	lover
salt	sodom
new	girl
habit	secret
pray	knees
money	man
silly	blush
despise	whip
finger	manipulate
jolly	masculine
bird	girl
walk	street
frog	shiver
try	succeed
hunger	love
white	undies
child	mine
speak	love
pencil	eye
sad	love
plum	testicle
marry	no
home	none
nasty	man
glass	transparent
fight	manhood
wool	man
big	genitals
carrot	man
give	love
doctor	operation
frosty	female

Doctor	*Julian*
flower	vagina
beat	man
box	prisoner
wait	operation
cow	woman
name	Juliet
luck	operation
say	love
table	love
naughty	sex
brother	protector
afraid	operation
love	girl
chair	sex
worry	operation
kiss	female
bride	no
clean	girl
bag	hide
choice	woman
bed	woman
pleased	girl
happy	girl
shut	man
wound	operation
evil	man
swim	thighs
go	girl
paper	money
wicked	man
old	man
family	no
door	out
insult	man

" The Doctor's interest in the result of this word-association test lay in the quite unusual responses to his dictated words. In every case there was a deep significance behind each response-word.

" Reading down the list of Julian's words—almost every one of them has a sexual or a hidden significance. The repetition of the word ' love ', and the word ' girl ', the introduction of such unusual words as sodom, whip, carry, naked, manipulate, man, masculine, undies, testicle, vagina, operation (often repeated), thighs and so on, laid bare Julian's mind. His reactions were a perfect picture of his subconscious pre-occupation with sex, love, the operation and the feminine gender.

"A patient suffering from an over-anxiety complex would fill his list with 'worry-words' reflecting his particular state of mind", concluded Julian's brother. "In Julian's case, it was quite obvious what was the content of **his** mind and his pre-occupation with fear-thoughts in regard to the impending operation. There was, also, great play on the theme of love—generally an ever-present thought in the feminine mind".

8

JULIAN—NIGHT-CLUB STAR

" Julian ", wrote his brother, dealing with that period between the first burst of newspaper publicity and the operation, " was suddenly all agog to present himself to a live public, and, against my advice and that of Sandra's, agreed to appear at the Golden Dome night club in Golden Square, in London's Piccadilly.

" Julian could not sing, as was usual from a night club artiste, neither could he dance above the normal expected of the ballroom or Twist and Madison disciples. It was therefore a source of concern to Sandra and to myself exactly what he **would** do to justify a £50-a-week appearance at the Golden Dome.

" The theatrical agent who signed Julian up said that it would be quite enough for the publc just to be able to see him on stage, dressed in female clothes. So it was arranged that Julian was to compére the cabaret—introducing the various acts with a little patter that would give the audience several chances to see him and to hear his voice and to wonder at the enigma that was him.

" Julian started to attend the night club by day to be rehearsed in his lines. He was to appear differently dressed on each of six occasions during which he would have to introduce the acts on stage. The night club was small, with a tiny dais upon which strip-dancers and vocalists appeared under brilliant spotlights.

" It was arranged that he would appear in a long, clinging silver lamé evening dress, then in a short white cocktail dress, then in a tailored suit, a gay summer dress with a flared skirt, then in tapered slacks and shirt and, lastly, in brief sun shorts and sun-top. This delighted him, and he spent many hours in the flat trying on all the costumes and preening himself in front of the mirror.

" As he put on each outfit, he looked more and more feminine. His figure was perfect. Better than it had ever before been. His bust was now fully developed, his waist slim, his long legs smooth, his thighs had rounded and thickened towards the top in true feminine style. A film studio make-up expert came to the flat to direct him in stage make-up. A hair stylist was engaged to call at the flat each day to style his dark, lustrous hair. He even had an elocutionist, engaged by the theatrical agent, to improve his diction and to teach him voice projection.

"Everything was done to make his appearance at the exclusive Golden Dome a fabulous success. As the day drew near for the night of his first appearance, he grew more and more excited and positively sparkled. Pre-publicity was, by that time, appearing in the entertainment columns of all leading daily and evening newspapers. Already, the name 'Juliet' was appearing on playbills outside the club and in the press promotion. Even before the operation, 'Juliet' was born.

"As an advertising 'teaser' he was featured in six thirty-second television spots to advertise his opening at the club a week before the night. He made a brief appearance full-length on the small screen, with the Golden Dome as a background. An invisible voice off-screen asked him who he was, and he had to reply that he was Julian, and would be appearing at the Golden Dome as Juliet as from such-and-such a date. The thirty-second spot ended in a full-face fade-out of Julian smiling into the camera—one eyebrow arched in a provocative fashion.

"The commercial was followed by a spate of letters from indignant religious dignitaries deploring the moral decline of Great Britain, etc., etc., irate women annoyed at being usurped from their truly feminine pedestals, an angry note or so from Equity. Quite a deal of the letters were printed in the press, which added, free of charge, to the publicity build-up for Julian's opening at the Club.

"He was treated as a great darling by the rest of the artistes at the Club. There was not a trace of jealousy. The girls of the resident Club dance troupe made a great fuss of him, as did the other female artistes. The men who were appearing in the bill seemed quite fascinated and treated Julian with a great deal of respect.

"Big blow-ups of Julian's face and full-length photos of him appeared outside the entrance and in the foyer. The entertainment at the Club started at midnight and the show went on for an hour and a half. This would mean an entirely different routine for

Julian. He would never be in bed before two-thirty any morning and would spend half the day asleep. Already he was starting at the small end of the vicious circle from which, ultimately, there could be no escape.

" Julian's first-night appearance was a great success. The audience—packed to capacity—wanted more of him than the artistes whom he announced. There is no doubt that he carried the whole thing off magnificently. There were no cat-calls or wolf-whistles—no suggestions whatsoever that the audience found him crude or repulsive. His great overnight success recalled that of Barbette—once-famous European female impersonator who took the entire world by storm in the nineteen-twenties.

" This magnificent success, even before the operation had taken place, led his many new friends to wonder why Julian should bother at all about having the operation. It seemed that he was so well able to carry off his impersonation that the operation for a part of his body no audience, in public at any rate, would ever see, was totally unnecessary.

" But Julian's success as a transvestite was only a surface affair. Merely a means of putting him on stage, giving him an audience, pleasing that side of his nature that demanded acclamation of Julian as a man-turning-into-a-woman. The whole thing was still merely on the surface. Underneath, Julian knew he was still, virtually speaking, a man. And no one member of the nightly audience that watched him as he appeared at the Club for a twice-extended season understood the great desire tugging at Julian's heart-strings to make the thing a *fait accompli*—to be—as near as was humanly possible—a physical woman. The appearances in the night club were superficial and had nothing to do with the deep-down inner conflict that demanded a place for him, in society, as a woman and not merely a sensational night club artiste.

" Into Julian's life now came many perverts and inverts, intent upon cashing-in on his success, desiring to pry into his private life, intoxicated by his success and his ethereal, un-explainable beauty and unearthly sex-appeal.

" Julian now took his place on the short list of famous personalities who had changed their sex, such as Roberta Cowell, Christine Jorgensen, Coccinelle, April Ashley, and so on.

" As the decades roll by, from time to time there appears a man who becomes famous through such an affliction and such a triumph over Nature. Julian Griffiths was undoubtedly one of them. But, in his case, he became famous the world over before the final operation.

" In the world of athletics, there arise, from time to time, several suspect cases where it seems female runners are more masculine than feminine. But in show business, the incidence of such cases is pretty high. It is not so much that show business induces or encourages or cultivates such a condition as it is a case of such individuals ending up in show business.

" Julian steered well clear of the perverts, looking on them with some sympathy, but showing no interest whatsoever in their particular kinks. He looked upon himself as a perfectly normal person. The fact he was changing into a woman never seemed to strike him as being unusual. And that was one of the greatest secrets of Julian's success. He **was**—as he **wanted** to be. He **was** a woman—and so it **was.** And all who saw him, in private life and at the Club—acknowledged that fact—and did not seek to decry or deny.

" If this ", wrote Julian's brother, " was the measure of his pre-operational success—what of the days when the operation was over and he was **all** woman ? Would the success of the operation rob him of the pre-operational glamour that made him an object of wonderment because he was still half man and half woman ? Would a successful operation give him nothing else for which to live ? Would he feel the ultimate had been reached—that now, he **was** a female and the magic of being a man-woman no longer existed ? Was not the whole mystery and magic existent in the fact he had male organs as a female, female breasts as a male ? Would men still wonder and women still admire and envy—once there was little evidence left that he **was** basically a man ? Would show folk still want him ? Would audiences flood to see him ?

" The night club appearances went on and on, it seemed, with ever-increasing success, until the days grew shorter and autumn and winter approached—the season before early spring of next year, when the operation would take place ".

PART FOUR

THE OPERATION — AND AFTER

1

FINAL PREPARATIONS

" Throughout that winter, Julian continued to appear, not only at the Golden Dome, but at quite a few other night spots in town. He made a mint of money that would more than amply pay the costs of his expensive operation and leave a lot over for the difficult, inevitably inactive post-operation days ahead.

" There were more medical check-ups with Doctor Maxfield, and the specialist from the hospital at Casablanca paid more than one visit to Julian at the flat. Once again, Doctor Maxfield and the specialist tried to dissuade Julian from going through with the operation—but he was adamant.

" A certain hard quality had crept into Julian since his fabulous success at the night spots and after all the press publicity.

" I felt ", wrote Julian's brother, " further away from him than ever before. Gone were the days when Julian seemed a simple enough sort of person, intent on the crusade he felt himself to be carrying out for those hapless individuals born as he had been born. Public acclamation seemed to have spoilt him.

" He still went on seeing Sandra very often, and it seemed the strange affair between them was deepening. She was not one whit jealous of his success, and would wait on him after shows sometimes into the early hours of the morning, seeing he got his rest, making appointments for him, interviewing the Press on his behalf. She was a glorified secretary.

" Winter dwindled away into spring, and suddenly it was April, the fateful month in which Julian and I would travel together to Casablanca.

" Sandra and Julian suddenly decided to go on a week's holiday to the South of France just before the trip to Casablanca was due. There was nothing I could say—so off they both went.

" During that time away from me, Julian wrote me three letters in a row. The first two dealt with trivialities of their holiday, but the third was the longest—and reflected his attitude towards the impending fateful move he was to make on his return from the South of France.

(This particular letter Julian's brother gave to the Clinic towards the Case History of Julian—as it was a significant and rather touching document and, in a way, a form of last will and testament should anything go wrong and he should not survive the operation. It is here reproduced in full).

Villa d'Est,
South of France.
April, 19.........

My dear Brother,

Forgive me for spending these last few days away from you, with Sandra, in France. It must seem rather selfish of me. But I felt I just had to get away from all the old associations that London means, so that I could adjust my frame of mind better for what is to come.

Sandra is being wonderful. If I were a real man—I would have married her ages ago. As it is, I love her, as you must by now realise, with all the love my peculiar nature can bring forth—but I love her as a man and a woman, which is all really rather complicated !

I am sitting in the French sunshine, writing this. Sandra is lying beside me in a fabulous white bikini and, looking down at her, I feel crazed with happiness deep down inside of me, for I know that, soon, I also will be just like her . . . I sometimes think back to our poor mother and father, who were both such ordinary, conventional folk. But, in mother, there lurked a twisted little demon. For you know, brother, that it was she who first instilled into my puny mind the thoughts of femininity—in those far-off days when she paraded me in front of her gushing and no doubt perverted women friends in petticoats and dresses.

She turned me into a parody of her wishful dream for a girl-child. And, finally, she knew the damage she had done that day at the flat when she saw me for the first time **as** a girl.

Poor old father! He was so mixed up in his loyalties, he did not know which way to turn, did he? He never really quite got over the fact that he lost a son but gained a daughter—as they say—but not in the usual manner! However, I am glad they are both dead. This operation business, I feel, would have worried them both very much. When they were alive, I don't think either of them **really** thought I was serious about having one. To father, it was really too, too drastic; and to mother—well, the blood-tie made her feel the pain of the thing, if you know what I mean. And mother never **could** bear pain or suffering, for herself or for others.

Well! This time next week I will be lying on a bed in the hospital at Casablanca. You will be staying at an hotel a mile or so away, waiting to escort Juliet back to England! And Sandra will be staying at our flat, keeping the kettle on for our triumphant return!

I feel I owe you some sort of an apology for my behaviour over the last six months or so. Well, I'll say the night club racket went to my head. All those people looking at me night after night. All that adulation. All that money. I expect you felt I was drifting away from you. Perhaps I was, and I write now to say I am sorry. I know all you have done for me these last years while I have been re-developing. I owe an everlasting debt of gratitude to you, brother. I am fully aware of the great strength you have poured into me all this long time. How you have shielded me from ridicule, explained me away to curious, stupid, boorish folk, until they have learned to accept me.

And I realise how well you have handled my affairs, fixing things so that my money has been invested well against possible future poverty when I might well be a human wreck, neither man nor woman, with no place at all in any kind of society.

With those things in my mind, and my deep gratitude for them, and the debt I owe to you—I have seen to it that, in the event of my not surviving the shock of the operation, or dying under the anæsthetic or something horribly conventional like that—all my cash, all my investments will be yours, brother, every penny. And also my Diaries and notes and researches into my condition, for what they are worth, in case you can turn them into profit as a work on trans-sexuality. In any case, if I do survive, I sincerely hope you will assist in the publication of some sort of document that will let the world know how deep is such a problem as mine.

As to my future with Sandra—this is in the lap of the gods. I do not know exactly what will be her final reactions if the operation is a success and I am transformed into a woman. I feel that, basically, her love for me exists in the fact that I am a man—though a queer sort of man at that! In all our love scenes together over these past years—it has mostly been the masculine element in me that has been the ultimate between us. What she will feel and think when that masculine element has gone for all time I do not quite know. Perhaps she will wish me to leave altogether!

Well, brother, as they say—that is all for now! Keep this letter in particular, as it will confirm what I have said in my will, which you will find lodged with —— if the emergency should arise. Meanwhile, I look forward to seeing you again at the flat this coming week-end—and to making the final preparations for our journey together—to Casablanca and the future—first thing next Monday morning.

Yours affectionately,
Julian.

2

TRIP TO CASABLANCA

"At last", recorded Julian's brother, "the fateful morning arrived on which Julian and myself were to begin the trip to Casablanca. The day began well with fine weather and, by the time our plane was well in the air, the sun was shining brightly. We had said farewell to Sandra. Julian especially. There had been tears in her eyes as she saw us through the barrier on to the airfield. She knew that, next time she would set eyes on Julian, he would be a woman—perhaps far from her reach, now, for ever. And, again, there was the dreadful risk that, when he returned, he would be mentally or physcially deformed, never again to lead any sort of a rational life—either way.

"There were reporters at the airport, for the Sunday papers had been following Julian's adventures and had started to continue the weekly instalments. Photographs of Julian and myself were taken at the foot of the gangway; Sandra was taken with Julian alone. Later, I learnt that every evening and daily paper for the following twenty-four hours had carried news and pictures of our departure.

"That Julian's condition and brave attempt to overcome nature's handicaps was something that had caught the public's fancy was obvious. He was most certainly an international figure, féted as much as any film star.

"When we finally touched down at Casablanca, there were more reporters there also to meet us. More photographs were taken, more interviews recorded. A car from the Clinic to meet us and speed us away to the stark hospital.

"We were greeted by the specialist who was to perform the operation. After a pleasant meal, and introductions all round to the staff and nurses, in particular those attendant doctors and nurses who were to assist at the operation, Julian was ordered to bed and I went to the hotel at which I had booked a room for the duration of Julian's stay at the Clinic.

" Before I left, and after I had seen Julian tucked up in bed, I had a conversation with the principal female nurse who would witness and help at the operation on Julian. I asked her if she had attended any other cases of this sort.

" ' One or two ', she replied, ' but this is by far the most important and the most advanced '.

" ' What do you think of my brother ? ' I asked.

" She smiled. She was tall, dark and extremely attractive in her cool white uniform.

" ' He is a beautiful man ', she replied. ' It is quite tragic to see the female struggling within him to be let out '.

" ' You have no revulsion at the sight of a man in such a state of mind and body ? '

" ' He is a case ', she said, ' and a most interesting case. I have already seen him quite naked in the examination booth, and I think he is a wonderful person. I reacted to his undoubted masculine appeal but, as a woman, I was strikingly aware of a tremendous affinity. The other cases I have attended where sex-transformation has been atempted have been nothing like your brother. He is altogether fascinating and a challenge to medical science. I sincerely hope the operation is successful, for our sakes here, at the Clinic, as well as for your brother and for yourself.

" ' That man has a rare beauty that is difficult to describe. His eyes are so soft and feminine. I see in them years and years of mental anguish. His body is so smooth and feminine, yet, from time to time, as I watched him being minutely examined, I was aware of the **man** in him.

" ' He still is ', she said, ' very much a man. His sexual organs are very sensitive to touch and to the presence of females. There are no signs of atrophy and, in fact, he does not seem so insensitive to his masculinity as did another of the two cases I have mentioned seemed in pre-op days. One of them was completely incapable of any masculine manifestations of sexuality, whereas your brother dould, I am sure, perform the male sexual act with no difficulty whatever '.

" ' That is true ', I replied. ' And it worries me quite a lot. I wonder, sometimes, if, after the operation, Julian will not be dismayed at the absence of his masculinity—and a new kind of mental aberration will not set in '.

" The nurse smiled. ' That risk will obviously have to be taken ', she said. ' Your brother is determined to go through with it. He signed final papers in front of the specialist and myself to the effect he did this of his own free will. That he desired it. That he accepted full responsibility.

" ' No—I think that either the fantasy of femininity is too great for him to resist, or that his mental attitude is stronger than his male body. He certainly is no weak, feminine male. He is strong and robust. He was given a spermatozoa test in the examining room and achieved erection and orgasm in next to no time. I think his desire to be female is stronger than his body, and that his mind will safely take him over the border—provided the operation is successful and he survives '.

" ' Is death extremely possible ? ' I asked.

" ' The shock to the heart is considerable ', she replied. ' As well you must know, of course, as a psychologist ', she added. ' The act of complete castration is, in itself, violent enough. But the forming of a vagina from the flesh of the wound caused by castration adds to the enormous strain put on the nervous system. Add to that the constant risk of a hæmorrhage and the great prevalence of damage to the brain—and you have a very serious operation. But you know all this, of course ', she added.

" ' I was only trying to get a little consolation from you ', I replied.

" ' And—instead, I paint a very bad picture indeed. I'm sorry ', she smiled.

" ' We had a case ', she went on, ' where we made an artificial plastic vagina for the patient; but this, of course, prevents the new " woman " from having any real sexual feelings whatsoever. In Julian's—I mean your brother's case—we intend making use of the flesh surrounding his penis to fashion a vagina that will actually be part of his body, invested with nerve-ends that will respond to sexual stimulation. In that way—we hope to invest him with the sensitivity of a woman, the power to achieve the female orgasm as far as sensation is concerned.

" ' Of course ', she went on, ' the complete absence of ovaries will prevent the normal female function of the manufacture of female ova which, projected through the Fallopian tubes into the womb, creates the true female orgiastic sensations. But the nerves in the flesh from his penis—inverted—so to speak—should give him a great deal of sensation that will be a cross between the male and the female orgasm.

" ' If that method fails, well, then . . . ' she shrugged. ' He will be totally incapable of any sensation in the sexual act whatsoever, male or female. That, naturally, would be very bad for his mind, as there would be no climax to any emotional or physical activity in which he—as a woman—indulged. Frustration would be born and the whole sex transformation would be merely a surface thing '.

" ' Is it ', I asked, ' likely that the inverted-penis method will fail ? '

" ' It has been done once or twice before ', replied the nurse. ' Once with great success—once with complete and utter failure. But the specialist has great hopes that, on your brother, it will be a success '.

" I stayed at the hotel on that first night and thought of Julian asleep in the private room at the Clinic. The antiseptic, white, barren room that was to be his whole world for many weeks to come.

" I thought, into the long dark hours of the still night, of that body beneath the white sheets, bearing the top half of a female and the bottom half of a male. Of that divided mind. Of the long years of trial and trouble and conflict that had led up to this night when he lay in his room waiting for the dawn of the day upon which his operation was to take place.

" I wondered if it was all really worthwhile. Whether it might not have been just as well for Julian to have lived the mental life of a woman, and been content with that. The night club shows had given him fame. He had been adored from all sides—from backstage to front of the House. Why, I wondered, did Julian want to disappear into what might well be obscurity by being turned into a woman when, as a male with female characteristics, he was a sight for all eyes ?

" There was something mystical in Julian's firm resolve to have done with his male member. Was it a dark fantasy within the deep recesses of his mind that only he understood ?

" Was it because he wanted to be what his mother had always wanted him to be—a girl ?

" Was it a deep resentment against his father who wanted so badly to have a manly man for a son ?

" Was it rebellion against myself ? Did he want to be my **sister** ?

" I was worried, too, about the part Sandra would play in Julian's new life. I could not, for the life of me, see her feeling for him as she had felt for him in the past. I knew, and I feel sure she knows now, at this very moment, that it was and is the essential **bi-sexuality** of Julian that intrigues her and holds her to him.

" When there is no longer a male member to fascinate—what then ? When Julian begins well and truly to ape her sex, when he has nothing more to offer her than any other girl might have to offer—and not that, in true fact—would Sandra's devotion to him remain ?

" And what of myself ?

" With the long struggle over at last—would I feel that a certain part of my world with Julian had come to an end ? Would his hold over me disappear ? Would he become just an object of pity ?

" In the cold operating theatre, with its gleaming silver instruments and pitiless lights shining down on Julian's body tomorrow —would a whole new world of complexities be created ? "

3

THE LAST LONG HOURS

Julian recorded his impressions of the long hours of the night before the day of his operation and handed them to his brother just before he was given his pre-med. injection.

"At four o'clock tomorrow morning", wrote Julian, "I am to be given a sedative to enable me to sleep deeply. I am told I will awake from this at about ten in the morning and will then be given a final injection before I am taken off to the operating theatre. So now—from ten at night to four tomorrow morning— are my last long hours of conscious thought. After the final injection tomorrow at ten, I will know no more until the operation is done and I awaken from the anæsthetic to what, I am warned, will be weeks of pain that will be impossible for the doctors or nurses to drug away. It will be pain so great that no drug will relieve it.

"I now enjoy peace of body and mind for just a few hours more. What my mind will be like when faced with those long weeks of pain, I do not know. Let us hope that the knowledge the operation is a thing of the past and that I am well and truly female will help me over those terrible times to come.

"There is a tall, dark nurse attending me here and she reminds me of Sandra—except that Sandra has flame red hair. But there appears to be the same sympathetic approach and understanding. Her hand is cool and her dress rustles as she walks. She is a pleasing reminder of the femininity with which I am so obsessed. I am glad she is not huge and ungainly and the worst possible example of stiff, starchy womanhood. They have done well to make her my constant companion in these hours.

"I see her floating around my white room, smoothing the bedclothes, drawing the curtains, humming to herself as she works. And from time to time she comes over to me and puts a cool hand on my forehead. I feel, I hope for the last time, the male urges
148

rising within me. She fosters these emotions within my mind and my body, and doubt crosses my mind now, that I should sacrifice the power to love as a male.

"Bigger doubts begin to enter into my mind. I know that I have only to get up out of this bed, put on my clothes—and I shall be able to go to my brother and he will take me back to England again. That nothing will be said in reproach. That I would be able to assume my exciting night club life in London and live the same life as before—half man and half woman.

"Is it pride that holds me back from leaving the Clinic at this very moment ? Is it because of what Sandra, back in England, would think and say ? Or my brother ?

"But were I to die—would it matter so very much ? I would go down in medical history as the near-perfect case of trans-sexuality. My body would be dissected. My brain-cells would be probed in a search to discover the root of all this.

"But, if the operation is to be gloriously successful, and I am to emerge from this place in a few months' time as beautiful, as elegant, as desirable as any female could possiby be—then will it all not have been worth while ?

"The hours seem to have slipped by. My nurse has been in and out of my room. She has changed into a cool, light blue dress and dark blue apron. So unlike a nurse. A small white cap is on her head and she has made her face up again. In her I see myself. The same high cheek-bones, the arched eyebrows, the constant smile and the dark, dark hair. Her body, too, is like mine. And she moves and walks like me. Is she perhaps—not my nurse but a projection of myself that I see moving around my room ? Am I perhaps already in a delirium or under heavy sedation and the operation has started ?

"Outside—the deep Hospital clock strikes. Already it is three in the morning. In exactly one hour from now they will come to inject me and I will lose consciousness till the morning, only to be put to sleep again before the operation starts.

"In some way I feel as if I had only one more hour in which to live. That might so very well be true. In this dark hour I turn my mind towards God—something I will admit I have not done for many, many long years since this cross was placed before me. Would I blaspheme were I to compare myself with Him in the Garden of Gethsemane before the soldiers came for Him ? When he asked that the Chalice might be turned away from Him ? For He chose, as I have chosen, to have this cross. Perhaps, if I dare not be so presumptious, I can at least wonder exactly what is His opinion of what I am doing. Is this a sin against the flesh ? Is this the fornication of all fornications ? Is this an insult to the design of Creation ?

"Am I guilty of a sin against Nature as those who make H-bombs are sinners against Nature ? Do I seek to destroy ? Is this planned suicide with a fine edge to the blade—whether I die truly or live again as a woman but kill the man within me ?

"Dare I pray for survival ? For success ? Would that be profane ? I was born a man by the Will of God and now I seek to usurp this Divine intention and to re-create myself as a woman.

"In the face of things—this would certainly seem to be a blasphemy, a presumption. A direct challenge to the Will of God. But would it be a holy thing to have to go through the rest of my life gradually becoming more and more demented as I sought womanhood and never attained it ?

"And what of the other side to the question—that this evil thing has been wished upon me by the Will of God and therefore I seek to defeat it ? Can this frightful fantasy that has been breathed into me be the work of the Devil, and have I not the right to oppose ?

"Does not the original sin belong to my dead mother who sought to satisfy her unfulfilled desire for a girl-child by treating me as such in those far-off years ? Or to my father for being weak-minded enough not to see what my mother was about, and to stop her before it was too late ? Or to my brother, who has encouraged and helped me and seen to it that, this morning, I lie in this room waiting for the surgeon's knife ?

"A pathological state of mind can never be called a state of sin, surely. Many 'sinners' are victims to neuroses and compulsions that, to society and to the Church—appear to be wicked. But is not the minister of the Church himself a victim to his own private little neurosis and compulsion—a desire to escape from the world and its thousand-and-one responsibilities, trials and troubles ? Does he not sin, perhaps, in that he will not take up his crosses and oppose them; but prefers to hide behind the cloth of the priesthood so that he shall be inviolate and infallible. So that he may—in his little wooden confessional box—listen to the sins of others, and, in his un-wisdom and unsophistication—give empty and banal advice out of his inexperience? And chastise others for not being as strong as himself?

" Sex ", wrote Julian, " is not the biggest sin of Mankind, but the biggest neurosis.

" Now ", he went on, " I hear the clock striking half past three. I have just thirty minutes left for coherent thinking. When I wake later, I will be drugged almost immediately again, but far more deeply. So I know for sure I will not, after this last half hour is up—be able to think clearly and wisely again for a very long time. When I come from the operating theatre and **can** think again —my body will be so tortured with pain and confusion that rational thought will be impossible for a long time to come.

" In front of me pass the years, quickly and vividly, as they are supposed to pass before the mind's eye when one is dying. I see my home and my weak, foolish, misguided and doting mother and my failure of a father. My brother, growing up beside me manly, with no quirks of nature within his mind and body. I see Sandra as first I saw her. Her face when she first set eyes on me dressed as a girl—and recognised in me a kindred spirit.

" I recall those first adventurous walks with my brother in the London streets, dressed as a girl. The dances, the theatres, the stage of the night club with the eager faces of the audience looking up at me through a haze of blue smoke and vivid lights.

" What a wreck my life has been. But what an adventure also! I have lived not one life, but two! I have known the power of man and the weakness of woman. I have loved as a man and been loved as a woman.

" Very much as a condemned man might lie in his cell waiting for the sound of the Prison Governor and the priest who come to take him through the small door leading to the execution chamber —I lie in this bed in this room waiting for my nurse to come, with the specialist and the other doctors, to put me into my first sleep.

" The clock chimes the quarter.

" Now only fifteen minutes to go before their soft-padded shoes are outside the door of this room.

" I could resist this thing. I could refuse the injection. I could sit up in bed and say I had changed my mind. But once the needle has dug deep into my arm—there will be little chance any more,

of resistance. In a few hours I shall be too weak and too far away
to say anything.

"I know, now, that I am beginning to feel frightened. That
the over-weaning desire to be female weakens at this last minute.
That, before my horrified gaze run the horror-pictures of the operation to be performed on me. I see the bloody mess of it all. The
terrible finality of the act. I hear the tearing of living flesh, the
rasp of muscle and sinew as it is stretched away from my body.
I can see the great scarlet cavern where, for my life-time so far,
has been the symbol of my manhood. I can feel the tortured nerves
writhing in agony as they are cleaved from that flesh in which they
have dwelt since I was born. I can feel a great sorrow for the poor
white thing lying on the silver plate, never again to be used in
pleasure, never to create a new life within the body of a woman.

"And I wonder if this is not the insult of insults. This voluntary castration. This casting away of the Vessel of Life. Is this
worse than Sodom or Gomorrah ?

"I think of what my dark young nurse will have to witness.
How her gentle hands will touch those parts and perhaps carry
them away to be burned in white hot fire. How clinically cold and
scientific will be the doctors and the specialist as they work away,
stemming the flow of blood, watching my heart beats and my
breathing. Tying up the loose, dangling nerve-ends before they
wither away for ever. Working hard and desperately against a
thousand odds and time itself—to create, for me alone, the figment
of my imagination. To make, in that brilliant operating theatre—
a semblance of a woman-creature that I might have peace of mind
and satisfaction and solace for my compulsions.

"I see the nurse watching my breasts as they rise and fall—
to check how I breathe. I see her nurse's eyes running over me.
But surely she wil have some compassion—and see me as a woman
might see a man ?

"From a distance I now make out the sound of padded feet
as they walk the long, long corridor that leads to my room. The
clock is beginning to chime the hour of four. This is the last sound
I shall intelligently hear. I wonder, is my brother hearing also—
or is he sound asleep ?

"The footsteps are nearer now, and I can hear the clink of
instruments. The dull pinkish white light hanging in the ceiling
almost disappears as the door opens and the harsh light from the

long corridor enters the room. A flick of a switch and the room is flooded with more light.

" My nurse—cool, blue, dazzling, with a smile and limp, lustrous eyes, comes to my bedside and bears my arm. She swabs it with a puff of cotton wool. Now I see the specialist looming over the bed. A silver hypodermic is in his hand. He poises it above my arm.

" This is the moment in which I can cry out—cover my arm where the swab has cleaned it. Say it is all a mistake. That I want to leave. That I cannot see it through.

" But—my lips are dry. My throat constricted. My mind is screaming out to them to stop. But no sounds will come.

" I feel the needle thrust far down under the skin of my arm and know that it is no longer any use.

" My nurse begins to recede from me fast. She becomes a blur of blue and I can no longer see her face clearly. I see a smile on her lips that becomes an angry red gash before it disappears entirely. The shadow of the specialist looms above me and grows larger and larger. There seem to be other, indistinct figures in the room, moving around in a sort of grey gloom. The light in the ceiling grows blood red above me. My body begins to feel numb all over.

" Then all blacks out. And I can no longer resist ".

(The description of the last moments before he went under were added to this account of his last hours of freedom by Julian after the operation.)

The Clinic reported that Julian slept the remainder of the night and, in the morning, was given the pre-med. Julian's brother was at his bedside for the short time Julian was conscious before the operation; but, of course, little passed between them at that time.

" I went back to the hotel that morning ", wrote Julian's brother, " with an awful feeling of finality hanging over me. Either I would see Julian again alive—but transformed—or I would see his dead body. The operation was scheduled to take about six hours if all went well. I was to visit the Clinic early that evening to be told the best—or the worst. The hours hung heavy over me and I could not settle down to anything ".

4

THE OPERATION

" Julian was given a final injection in the thigh before being wheeled off to the operating theatre. That was the beginning of four days' unconsciousness for him.

" Every time he was to awaken from his coma during that four days he was to be given a fresh injection to help allay the dreadful post-operational pains. Shock to the nervous system would be far too great after the operation for any human system to withstand.

" The operation ", wrote Julian's brother, " was in quite a few stages, unlike the normal operation for removal of the appendix or gall-stones. The operation was known, as well as a phallectomy, as a sexual hysterectomy.

" During those long, long hours of waiting, in the hotel and out, walking away dread thoughts and fears, I knew precisely what Julian was going through.

" I had ", continued Julian's brother, " a thorough knowledge of the operation. To the layman, the discarding of the male member would be like taking the skin from a cylindrical vegetable by cutting down each side of it, and allowing this skin or outer covering to hang in connected shreds round the bottom of the cylindrical object while, at the same time—cutting out the flesh or substance inside the skin. In effect—Julian's male member was divested completely of its outer covering, and the mass of flesh and nerves and tissue was torn away from the body from its tip to where it entered the body.

" Blood vessels were then cut with the knife, and, before the flow of blood became too great and uncontrolled, joined with others so that the flow of blood was maintained within the body and circulation kept up. The next stage was that the scrotum—

the bag containing the testicles—was removed and the ureter placed in a different position.

"This stage of the operation left Julian with what amounted to a gaping, bloody hole where before had projected his penis. This space, sinking back into his body, was to be the vagina, the formation of which was to be the next step in the operation.

"The hole was deepened in Julian's body and the remainder of his penis removed. In this way a clear, fleshy shaft was formed. Into this shaft were tucked the shreds of skin that, before, had been the outer covering of Julian's male member. These strands and shreds of flesh were placed inside the newly-formed passage and so provided a lining for it. This skin would, eventually, graft itself on to the living flesh of the wound and become part of it. The nerves and tissues in the strands of flesh were kept alive so that the passage formed in Julian's body would not be dead—but vitally living, vitally alive flesh—possessed of that sensitivity common to a woman's vagina.

"Action had to be quick, before the outer skin—devoid of the spongy substance it had before covered—died. At any cost—this skin had to be kept fresh, vital and alive.

"After that", continued Julian's brother, "the opening in Julian's body, lined with the loose skin, had to be filled with a wad of material in order to keep the wound distended, and to prevent it from closing up and the skin and flesh from growing together. This preventative plug would stay in Julian's body for a week or two until it was surgically safe to remove it and to know that the new-formed vagina would be self-supporting and would remain strong.

"Some artificial vaginas", went on Julian's brother, "were made of a soft substance, plastic in origin. But, in such cases, there would be no sensitivity, no nerve-ends to be titillated by touch or contact and the organ would be entirely impervious to pain or pleasure like the artificial roof to the mouth is in a set of upper false teeth.

"As the hours dragged by that day", recounted Julian's brother, "I knew that, if all was going well, a further stage in the operation would be taking place. This stage entailed moving the prostate gland and the seminal vesicle that that their positions were not opposed to the invasion of a vagina in Julian's body.

"It is generally known in medical circles that the seat of

woman's real sexual pleasure and sensation and gratification lies—
not in the vaginal passage as so many laymen think—but in the
highly sensitive tip of the clitoris, an organ which is, in the female,
the actual counterpart of the male penis. The clitoris can actually
become a small penis in the female if it is exercised and stretched
enough. So Julian, in order to be able later to enjoy the full
feminine sensations that would be due to him in his new role as a
complete woman, had to have a clitoris fashioned at the mouth of
his vagina.

"This was accomplished—not by creating a mound of flesh
at the opening—but by centreing certain nerve-ends so that they
formed a network of ultra-sensitivity by collectivity—near the
mouth of the vagina.

"The operation on Julian was doubly complicated in relation
to ordinary castration, in which the male member and scrotum is
only removed and the wound so made allowed to heal and the
urinary function only being re-created. Julian's new sexual organs
had to fulfill their sexual role from a feminine point of view, but,
as well as a complete vagina being formed from living flesh—his
urinary functions also had to be re-channelled and their adequate
and correct working assured. Also, the wall of the rectum, which,
in a woman, runs almost parallel with the wall of her vagina, had
to be conditioned to the new structure running alongside it.

"Naturally—there was no opening at the inside end of the
new vagina that, in the normal woman, gives access to her womb
and allows the invasion of male spermatozoa in the sexual act.
Neither, of course, were Fallopian tubes formed, nor was there to
be any suggestion of a womb. Julian would never be able to have
a child, or be able to manufacture female ova. Sexual orgasm
would consist of the heights of ecstasy achieved by inflammation
of the nervous systems within his vagina and in his newly manu-
factured clitoris. His natural voluptuousness and highly-coloured
imagination and inborn instincts as a woman would do the rest.

"Menstruation would never enter into Julian's new scheme
of things, either. His dominant desire for femininity would—in
line with the body-mind relationship pattern of symptoms, pains
and pleasures—give him the true sensations common to woman
and so much desired by him.

"After the operation—there would be delicate stitching—
anxious moments as the welling blood from the great, gaping

wound stemmed and began to re-enter the body and re-join the natural circulatory system. Julian's legs would have to be kept apart for some time to allow the healing process to commence. He would have to be strapped to his bed so that movement was impossible. For too much—or sudden jerky movement would tear the stitches out and the danger of hæmorrhage would be very great.

"And then there would be the first return to consciousness which would place a very great strain on the heart and the sympathetic nervous system.

"The agony on awakening would be indescribable. It would assault Julian from all sides. It would not only be centred on the bruised and assaulted parts of his body into which the surgeon's knives had dug deep—cutting this way and that with exquisite precision. The pain would well in on all sides, from his head down to his toes. His stomach would feel as if it had been turned inside out and his thighs as if every ligament and muscle had been separated and minutely and diligently scraped with a knife. The bottom of his spine—focal nerve centre for sexual sensation—would be a burning-point of fine fibres. His temperature would be dangerously high. Damage to his delicate brain cells and nerve-tissues would be acute and his sanity would hang in the balance.

"During those long hours of waiting", wrote Julian's brother, "I could see, in my mind's eye, Julian, lying on the operating table under the merciless glare of the lamps, surrounded by masked figures in olive-green operating gowns. The whole picture was one of total fantasy. For him—little of the conditioned privacy of a normal operation, for his whole body from the waist down would be bared to view and he would, although in a deep state of unconsciousness, be suffering indignities unknown to the average patient in an operating theatre.

"There would be a protracted stay in Casablanca while he was recovering, amounting to several months. It was quite on the cards that Sandra would not be able to contain herself and that she would fly out to see Julian long before he would be ready to return to England. I had a cablegram all ready to send to her, saying that the operation had been successful—as soon as I arrived at the Clinic to be given the news. I also had another cablegram prepared to say that the operation had been a failure, and yet another to say Julian had died. As I read and re-read them, I wondered which of the three I would **have** to send.

"Reporters were, I knew, hanging about outside and in the Clinic, waiting to send news to the papers for publication the world over. The great news value in Julian's story lay in the fact that he was such a wholly delightful person, such a fascinating enigma. So attractive—so very near approaching a true female and so un-freakish. His image had captured the world's imagination and aroused pity and wonderment all round. There had been hundreds of well-wishing telegrams and letters at the London flat before our departure—and more had been at the Clinic when we arrived.

"About late afternoon", Julian's brother wrote, "I had a long-distance call from the impatient Sandra from our flat in London. We spoke for quite a long time. She was quite obviously very much on edge. I told her I would cable her that evening and phone her the very next day.

"At last the hour arrived at the end of this dreadful day of suspense when I could return to the Clinic and know the worst—or the best.

"I walked through the few streets leading to the Clinic, which stood on top of a hill. It was an imposing looking place from the outside—tall, white and architecturally severe.

"Inside—long, clinically clean corrdors led off from a central reception hall. A spiral staircase led to the first, second and third floors. The operating theatre was on the second floor and a smooth lift carried patients and nurses right to the entrance, with room in which to carry a stretcher-trolley.

"As the clock was striking the hour, I mounted the steps of the Clinic and made my way up to the Reception Desk. A huddle of reporters sprang to life as I approached the desk and surrounded me—pencils poised over shorthand notebooks. But—before I could say a word, or anyone had any time to pose me a question—the specialist who had operated on Julian appeared.

"He took my arm and led me down the corridor towards his office".

SURVIVAL

" ' Your brother has survived ', said the specialist.

" The relief was tremendous ", recorded Julian's brother. " But—survival could mean that Julian was alive—but **how** alive ? The specialist reassured me ".

" ' He has come through the operation successfully ', he said. ' His heartbeats are strong and regular, his respiration normal, his pulse steady '. The specialist shrugged. ' But ', he added, ' as to your brother's state of mind when he finally steers clear of the necessity for drugs—and the pain has diminished—and he begins to feel something like a human being again—there is still little knowing. If the heart has withstood the shock of the operation so well—there is every hope the brain has not suffered. But the test will come when Julian awakens to continuous pain that cannot be relieved and that he will have to live with for at least three weeks. If he can surmount that obstacle and still keep his reason —then all should indeed be well '.

" ' Can I see him ? '

" ' He is, at present, still in a state of unconsciouness. The effects of the anæsthetic have not yet worn off. But, certainly, you may see him '.

" In the space of a few seconds ", continued Julian's brother, " I found myself in Julian's private room.

" I was looking down at the white face of a transparently beautiful girl, her lustrous black hair forming a dark halo on the pillow. Her eyes were closed. She was breathing rhythmically. Her lips were pale and there were dark rings under her eyes.

" I was so struck by the incredibly **new** appearance of the features. Gone now, it seemed to me, were all traces of masculinity. They had been few enough before, it is true, but now—the nose, the nostrils, the cheekbones, the lips, and the brows were so essentially feminine as to pass my understanding. It was, indeed, as if this man, Julian, had died, and that here lay his reincarnated body and soul in the image of a truly beautful girl.

"A lump rose in my throat as I looked down, saw this culmination of years and years of hard work, will and effort. I noticed the lacy frill of a nightdress and was aware of the infinite tact and humanity of the specialist in dressing Julian so, so that, when he awakened—he would be conscious of the softness of his attire. I was aware, also, as I looked round the room, of three vases of beautiful fresh roses dotted here and there. Of a fragrant perfume that seemed to linger in the air.

"The specialist divined my thoughts.

"'Yes', he said. 'We have made everything as feminine as possible for him, so that when he wakes—he thinks of himself as a girl and has no memories, as far as is possible, of his former masculine state. And, remember', he warned me, 'As soon as your brother wakes up and is able to hear people speak to him, myself, his nurse, the other doctors and, of course, most importantly, **yourself**—he must hear himself addressed as **Juliet.** Not Julian. The name of Julian, with all its unhappy associations, is likely to upset him and to make his task of getting better quickly, harder. By calling him Juliet, by treating him wholly and completely as a girl, by acknowledging the fact he **is** a girl—it will give him strength to fight his pain. It will give him the same satisfaction, happiness and peace of mind as that given to a woman when she has borne her first child and is acknowledged as a **mother.** You understand?'

"I nodded.

"Beneath the thin, pink sheets, I could see the breasts rising and falling. My eyes travelled the length of the bed and I could make out the figure stretched out—long, slim, vital. I marvelled at the way in which the face seemed to have cast off the final traces of manhood and had now become completely and utterly feminine.

"The dark-haired nurse came into the quiet, scent-laden room, over to the bedside.

"'She is lovely, isn't she?'

"The nurse pulled the sheets up around my brother's shoulders.

"'You have a beautiful sister now', she said.

"Later", went on Julian's brother, "I had an opportunity

of discussing with the nurse what went on in the operating theatre. I was staying at the Clinic until Julian—until **Juliet**—recovered consciousness for the first time. I had sent off the 'success' cablegram to Sandra and was sitting in the nurse's office.

" ' Was it very—hard ? ' I asked her.

" ' She seemed to resist in a strange, uncanny sort of way ', answered the nurse. " It seemed almost as if your sister wanted to hang on, at the very last moment, to that very thing that stood in the way of her future happiness. When the actual severance was taking place—Juliet stirred quite frighteningly—as if pain could be felt. But the anæsthetic assured us all that Juliet was completely under, and impervious and insensible to pain or feeling of any sort. It was almost as if her soul was rejecting what was being done to her at the actual time of crisis. As if a last-minute protest was being made '.

" ' Was the severance complicated ?'

" ' It is never easy ', she said. ' And, in this case, we realised it was a difficult operation. In spite of your sister's great femininity—she was, as a man—well-formed, strong and vital. Such a paradox ! '

" ' How can you—a woman—bear to see such things ? '

" ' I am a nurse ', she smiled.

" ' I can understand your bearing the sight of a normal operation ', I said, ' but this complete desecration of manhood—this completely cruel termination of personality and physical power— even to me, a trained psychologist, it seems it must have taken a great effort of will on your part to watch it '.

" ' Perhaps if your sister had been a true freak of nature, an ugly, deformed object—I might have found the sight repulsive and nerve-shattering. But Juliet—even before the operation—was such a beautiful human being that I felt only a great compassion and willed that it should be a success—that the severance should be clean, and whole and complete. For I knew that that was the only way in which that lovely creature would find happiness and peace of mind. I knew that the torturously vicious tearing away of the member was of itself an act of ultimate kindness '.

" ' I could never have borne watching it ', I said.

" ' You heal minds ', smiled the nurse. ' I help to heal bodies. You have your share of apprehension watching tortured minds trying to cut themselves away from tortured bodies '.

" I was reminded of Sandra ", went on Julian's brother, " in this nurse, and wondered how it seemed there were females who had sympathy with people such as my brother, and who were willing to help them in their struggles and did not find anything to disgust them in the spectacle of a man wishing to be a woman.

" Late that night the telephone rang in my hotel bedroom.

" It was Sandra.

" Her voice was loud and clear at that time, and we had a long conversation that ultimately cost us pounds.

" I assured her Juliet was alright—that she was breathing well, that no unforeseen complications had set in so far. Sandra said she could not bear the long wait until Juliet would be well enough to return to England, and that she could not face up to life without me to comfort her, so it was decided she should fly out that week-end, and I arranged to meet her at the air terminal on the following Saturday afternoon.

" I was glad—really. Her companionship would help pass the time away and, with Juliet's progress in common—the wait would not seem so long. I wondered what would be her reactions when she saw Juliet looking so lovely—so completely female. Whether her feelings would change, or whether her strong Lesbian streak would maintain them—on a different level.

" The specialist had said he did not think Juliet would awaken that night; at least, not until the early hours of the following morning, when vitality would be at its lowest ebb. He suggested I called again the next morning about ten. He warned me that Juliet might well be in delirium from the pain she would be suffering and would not easily recognise me. This, said the specialist, would wear off as the days went by, but conversation would be very difficult for many long days while Juliet was adapting herself to suffering and the pain was slowly diminishing.

" After the phone call from Sandra, I went to sleep with some great relief. At last, the actual nightmare of the operation was over. Had Juliet died, it would have been such a waste of medical and psychological thought and planning over the long years when the first signs of a sex-change first made themselves apparent.

" Perhaps now, I thought, there will be peace for us all ".

6

THE TORTURED WEEKS

" Sandra flew out and I met her at the Casablanca Airport ",
wrote Juliet's brother. " Then began three weeks of torture for
poor Juliet and terrible anxiety for Sandra and myself.

" Juliet hovered between life and death—her body wracked
with pain that could not be quietened. There were no known drugs
that could completely drive away the agony. It was insistent, all
of the time; drugs and injections only succeeded in taking the
sharpest edge off.

" Juliet ran a high temperature and was only just able to recognise Sandra and myself when we paid our usual twice-daily visit
to see her. Usually, she was rambling on in a species of delirium,
capable only of moving her head from side to side on the pillow,
as her body had to remain strapped to the bed in case violent
spasms or contortions ruined the vital healing process that was
slowly taking place.

" Sandra cried each time we left the Clinic, and slept very
little at night. We were both in constant touch with the Clinic
in case a serious crisis should arise.   The specialist assured us
Juliet had a very strong heart and that, provided her morale
remained as high as it had so far, and the will to live stayed with
her—she would overcome this period.

" ' Is all this suffering really worth it ? ' I asked Sandra, after
one of our visits.

" 'Juliet is a mystic ', she replied. ' She is Divinely inspired.
I believe she has been able to place herself in a self-hypnotic
trance, that she went into this automatically-induced state since
before she had the final injection just before the operation and
that now she is experiencing its post-hypnotic effects '.

" ' How she must hate all to do with sex and the body at this
moment—if she can reason that way ', I said. ' And how she must

hate everyone who has had a hand in bringing her to this dreadful crisis in her life. Her mother, her father, myself—and . . . '

" ' Me ? '

" I nodded. ' And you '.

" ' When a mother is experiencing the pains of child-birth ', said Sandra, ' she hates all to do with sex and the body. Hates her husband, too. But—as we know—once it is all over and the child has been born—a merciful veil falls over her mind, blotting out the memory of all she has been through. So she is able to face having another child—and still more. I think a veil will fall over Juliet's mind when these times have passed—and that she also will forget all her sufferings '.

" ' I hope so '.

" Two weeks later, Juliet had a sudden relapse ", went on the brother's report. " Her life hung in the balance for four anxiety-ridden days. She was suffering far less pain but her mind was aware—for the first time since the operation—of the things that had been done to her and her thoughts were, in delirium, divided between the enormity of her sacrifice and her relief that the operation was now over.

" Juliet remembered enough of these dangerous, death-kissed twilight hours to write down her thoughts and feelings during that time ".

(These thoughts were typed and added to the general Dossier. They appear in the following chapter.)

7

JULIET'S FIRST CONSCIOUS THOUGHTS

" The air ", wrote Juliet, looking back on the time of his sudden relapse at the Clinic, " is laden with scent. I identify this scent with a high-pitched pain that seems to run through me from head to toe. Forms that look like flowers are around my room, which is all white, with slips of sunshine latticed across the walls.

" Vague thoughts that once I was a man keep drifting through my mind. But I am wearing a nightdress and a fragrance seems to hang about me. Then I remember. The room with Sandra. She is making my face up. Or I am dressed in a short white skirt. None of it is quite clear.

" Then I am walking down the street arm in arm with my brother. Glancing in a shop window—I see that I wear a short skirt. I have high-heeled shoes. My hair falls almost to my shoulders.

" All that seems countless years ago. I remember—above the searing pain—that I have had an operation. And I begin to sweat with fear at the thought of what I have done to myself. Have I crippled and maimed myself for the rest of my life ?

" I try to rise from this bed but my legs are bound tight. Only my arms are free. I try to sit up but there is also a band round my waist that holds me to the bed. I call out for someone and the nurse comes in. The dark nurse who looks a little like Sandra. I ask her to hold a mirror to my face so that I can see what I look like. The pains well up inside me—spread out all over me. I can feel hot sweat on my forehead but I feel icy cold inside.

" The nurse comes over to the bed and holds a mirror over my face. Looking up into it, I can see a dead white face against a pink pillow.

" It is **my** face.

" It is thin but beautiful. There are dark rings under the eyes.

165

The cheek-bones stand out with deep shadows behind them. I can see now that this is the face of a girl. My face.

"Then the pains grow all over me again. My hips ache and my stomach is pierced with a million sharp knives.

"I know I am thinking all this out loud. The nurse has called in the specialist and now I think I can see my brother standing beside the bed. Behind him seems to be Sandra—but that cannot be, of course—for Sandra is nowhere near here.

"Am I a man or a woman?

"My lips frame these words, but neither the specialist nor my brother answers me and Sandra just looks down at me. In any case—I am sure she isn't really here at all.

"I wonder, at this moment, if I will ever leave this white room that smells of heavenly perfumes and that seems to be festooned with flowers. Whether I will ever walk again, or talk properly to people who seem to be able to hear me talk and who will answer me.

"I wonder will I ever be able to walk again? I feel as if I had no legs at all—as if I did not exist any more from the waist down. Perhaps I am paralysed and that is why I cannot feel anything but wave after wave of pain. Perhaps I am imagining I feel pain in my legs but they are really quite dead. I am happy with the sight of my face, even though it does look terribly thin and wasted. Perhaps some day I will be able to eat good food again, and to drink, and to appear in front of hundreds of people every night.

"The enormity of what I have done creeps over me. I am at once afraid and contrite, as if I had committed a great sin and that this is my punishment—to lie here, in this bed, in this white room, for all time, unable to move or to lift my head. Feeling that I am living only down to my waist, that the rest of me is non-existent.

"Perhaps I have been too vain and proud, too arrogant. Too eaten up with myself. Perhaps I should have been contented with the body I was given and not sought to change it in this way.

"Probably, if I ever do escape from this place, I will be, for the rest of my life, some indeterminate creature—neither man nor woman. I shall never be able to love, and I shall never be loved. I shall be a repulsive creature to the whole world. I shall grow old and withered, or develop a cancer in my body because of the terrible things I have let happen to it. Or I shall gradually go out of my mind and spend the rest of my life in a lunatic asylum.

" Is it **possible** for the human system to suffer so much, for so long ? Has medical science **really** perfected this terrible operation—so that one **really** survives and goes on living a normal, rational life ? Or is it all a great illusion, dreamt up by doctors and psychologists, to give them all a chance to experiment with the human body and mind ?

" Somewhere in this place is a white dress. I brought it here and said I wanted to wear it when I left this place. Is it hanging up on a hanger in some dark wardrobe—waiting for me to claim it ? Will the day ever come when I will, in bright sunlight, walk down the steps that lead away from this place, arm-in-arm with my brother—to greet the world as a woman ?

" The specialist is moving to the side of the bed now. The dark nurse has bared my arm and is wiping it clean. Now—I feel the hot needle the specialist holds piercing my flesh. For a second or so the pain of it cancels out all my other pains. But then the other pains return doublefold.

" But mercifully—not for long. A sense of dullness and numbness is creeping over me. I believe the pain, for the very first time for such a long, long time, is receding. I begin to feel soothed and calmed. The specialist, my brother and the ghostly Sandra are fading from sight. They are becoming just dark shadows and this white room is growing grey.

" Still the scent of roses hangs in the air. This perfume is the last thing I remember as I slip away ".

" Juliet slept under the influences of that injection for the very first time since the operation was over ", wrote Juliet's brother. " She slept for almost forty-eight hours. When she awakened, the crisis was over and she began to make splendid progress.

" Now—the visits to the Clinic every day were better and better. Juliet recognised Sandra for the very real person she was, and she was released from the straps that bound her to the bed and was able to sit up.

" Sensibility returned to her mind and sensation to her body. Now she knew, for certain sure, that she **was**, indeed, the female she had so craved to be.

" Her face began to fill out. She became even more radiant

than before, when I had first set eyes on her immediately after the operation. The specialist described her case as the most perfect he had ever experienced.

" Now—reporters were granted interviews with the specialist and myself ", continued Juliet's brother. " Soon the whole world knew of the success of the operation and photographs of Juliet sitting up in her bed at the Clinic were given world-wide publication. The English Sunday newspaper sent over the medical correspondent who had first interviewed us all at the week-end cottage so that the weekly Sunday feature could be continued.

" All this meant more money for Juliet and she was now a very rich girl. The biggest London night club sent out a contract for her to sign to appear as soon as she returned to Town.

" Pretty soon Juliet was allowed to get out of bed and to walk around the grounds of the Clinic. Progress was slow at first but, after a day or so she was able to walk quite normally.

" Then came the day when she asked to be allowed to see herself for the very first time quite naked, full-length in a mirror. A long mirror was taken into her room and the specialist, Sandra and myself left her to undress.

" Ten minutes after we had left her she opened the door and asked us all in. She had put on a nightdress and house coat and was busy at her dressing table, lately installed, brushing her long, dark hair. As soon as we came in she greeted us with a radiant smile. Happiness was written all over her face. She asked if we could arrange, as quickly as possible, for a photographer to come to her room to photograph her completely nude.

" The specialist nodded assent. He realised this was inevitable, as Juliet naturally wanted to record this great moment for all time.

" That afternoon a photographer called and took photos of her in the nude. Later we learnt that he hastened to sell copies to many Continental magazines and that they appeared a few days later—all over Europe.

" So it was that Julian went for ever—and Juliet was born.

" She was certainly a wonderful sight. Her body was perefctly proportioned. Where—before—had been the male genitalia—now existed the soft female pelvis centred perfectly between shapely thighs. Her breasts had grown larger with the disappearance of her last traces of masculinity. Her hair was longer, more lustrous. Her eyes were deeper-set, her waist even slimmer.

"Here indeed was a great miracle of medical and psychosomatic science".

THREE SPECIALIST OPINIONS ON PROBLEMS OF TRANSVESTITES AND HOMOSEXUALS

" In the reference library at the Clinic ", wrote Juliet's brother, " I found many documents and articles and papers, as well as complete magazine features, devoted to the problems of the sex-change man and woman, homosexuals and Lesbians.

" Here are three opinions, voiced by leading authorities, on transvestites and homosexuals :

" ' The famed English psychiatrist and criminologist, Dr. Norwood East ', (said " **Realife Guide** ", American Sexology publication), ' conducted research among transvestites. " Although homosexuals may dress up as women to increase or vary their attraction to other men ", he wrote, " the true male transvestite obtains sexual gratification from pretending to be a woman, and his fantasy is faciliated by wearing her clothing.

" ' " In appearance, manners and interests, they seem and feel more feminine than masculine and naturally adopt the little characteristic mannerisms of women. It is important to distinguish this type from the homosexual as they pass their lives with no sign of sexual interest in their own sex ".

" ' From the above, it is apparent the transvestite adopts feminine characteristics because feminine clothing goes hand in hand with girlish habits.

" ' Medical men have found that transvestites have inherent doubts about their own virility. " Penis-inferiority " is the term used to describe such persons.

" ' When garbed in feminine apparel, this type of man receives some release from the fear that he may be inadequate sexually.

" ' He is a victim of a castration complex.

" ' But, dressed as a woman, his complex melts away since he feels himself in the passive role of a woman. When these tensions are gone, his sexual powers become restored because of the lowering of inhibitions '.

"Speaking of such persons, Frank S. Caprio, M.D., says (in the same American magazine) : ' Physiologically there is nothing wrong with his sexual apparatus. But psychologically, he harbours neurotic fears associated with the sex act, which figuratively speaking, is equivalet to a feeling of no longer possessing a penis or of it being amputated. In many cases guilt is the predominant factor involved '.

"Here follows a short account of a married partnership—in which the husband was a transvestite :

" ' When Paul married Shirley, he was already a lover of feminine garments. Paul had been the idol of his mother's life. His father had long deserted them. Paul's mother instilled in the youth the feeling of antipathy against his father and men in general. Paul doubted his own manhood. He was taught that all men were cruel and selfish and could apply this theory to himself as well. His mother gave him dresses to wear and tried to keep him as feminine as possible. He grew up in her image and adopted her characteristics as well as his compulsive urge to wear feminine clothing.

" ' Following marriage, Paul had to put on frilly undergarments, even dresses, silk stockings, etc. Shirley felt ill at ease but she saw that Paul could fulfil marital relations only when girlish clothes restored his sense of adequacy. When dressed as a male, he associated his own manhood with the seeds of hatred against males implanted by his over-possessive mother, and he could not function. Transvestism, when blended into the married life as such, offered Paul and Shirley a satisfactory relationship.

" ' By nature, most women are passively inclined ', goes on the author, Joseph Mellister, M.D., in the magazine. ' Of course, there are exceptions and many women exhibit signs of extreme aggressiveness, more so than the most virile male. But there are, conversely speaking, many men who are the passive type. They cling to transvestism as a garment of passivity.

" ' They feel perfectly secure when wearing a silk dress, long silken hose which is fastened to a garter strap, even when wearing a silk print dress of wine colour with a beige jacket which looks simply heavenly on them.

" ' These feminine garments restore their self-security in their sexual powers and they no longer feel guilty about being the passive member in sexual relations. Transvestism offers the impetus and aphrodisiac to their powers and they are able to function sexually.

" ' Many marriages may thus survive with an extremely passive husband who would otherwise be impotent were it not for his transvestite security. Dressed as women, they felt secure '.

" ' Transvestism may have one of its roots in the protest against one's own sex role and is closely related to . . . fetishism ', says Dr. Hugo G. Beigel, in the Encyclopædia of Sex Education.

" He explains further that when parents dress a boy as a girl, giving him a feminine name and convince him that he is the daughter they want but could not have, these are additional causes that prompt urges towards transvestism.

" ' The man who finds he cannot function sexually without wearing feminine clothes may adjust himself to his world of cross-dressing in marriage if he is able to find a right thinking woman; preferably, one who is more interested is satisfying and mutual sex pleasures and enjoyment, rather than the social dictums that tell them how it must be obtained '.

" The Rev. A. Mallidie Smith, writing in the B.N.A. News, said : ' Before the Reformation, sexual misbehaviour, including homosexual behaviour, was dealt with by the Church courts—in other words, it was regarded as a sin but not a crime. But in 1533, for the first time, the act of buggery was made a criminal offence. The maximum penalty was death, which was reduced in 1861 to the present maximum of imprisonment for life. This type of behaviour is equally criminal if committed by a man with a woman, whether they are married or not; but recently the law has been applied only where two men are involved. Homosexual behaviour as such was not a criminal offence until 1885, when a clause making all such behaviour punishable was inserted without any discussion into a Bill dealing with female prostitution.

" " So we now have the strange situation whereby if a man wishes to live with a woman outside marriage, he is legally free to do so; a woman may have sexual contact with another woman without incurring any risk of legal interference; but any sexual relationship between two men is punishable by law. A law as anomalous as this, and with such a dubious history, can surely be justified only if it can be shown to be necessary for the moral health of the community. But, far from this being the case, its effect is mainly harmful.

" 'Very few homosexuals are deterred by fear of the law from indulging in homosexual behaviour. Those who exercise self-control do so from religious or moral motives.

" 'On the other hand, many men who are otherwise decent and responsible are driven to adopt the attitude that it does not matter whether their partnerships are based on genuine affection or whether they are merely sordid, whether their actions take place in private or in a public place, or whether young people are involved; since whatever they do is equally a crime.

" 'Nor is it true, as is sometimes asserted, that stable private relationships are immune from legal interference. The curiosity of neighbours, the exchange of letters which subsequently fall into other hands, information laid by previous associates in the course of a police investigation, can and do lead to legal proceedings and imprisonment. The effect of what may well be a deep personal friendship being described publicly in court in purely physical terms can be disastrous. It cannot make the men less homosexual; but it may drive them to lead a life of promiscuity, and at the very least it leaves them with a permanent sense of bitterness and injustice, heightened often by the knowledge that their careers are ruined.

" 'Weaker characters suffer acute mental distress through fear of the law, leading sometimes to suicide or attempted suicide, and often to a thoroughly anti-social frame of mind. Such men need expert advice and treatment, but are the least likely to seek it while fear of the law remains. Others seek refuge in marriage, which is likely only to cause unhappiness to the wife and is almost certainly doomed to failure. For it is not only homosexuals who are harmed by the present law. Wives, relatives and friends can all be involved.

" 'Many people fear that, if the law were changed, men with only slight homosexual tendencies would be encouraged to give way to them. In fact, this has not been the experience of countries where the law has been reformed, nor does it seem to apply to female homosexuality in this country.

" ' Few people who are capable of achieving the security of a happy marriage would sacrifice it to a life of increasing isolation; and " borderline " cases are far less likely to seek advice now than they would be if the law allowed them to discuss their problems openly. In fact, of course, human emotions are not controlled by legal enactments. No man can feel attracted by women because the law tells him he should, any more than most men would cease to seek a partnership with a woman if hetersexual behaviour were illegal.

" The blackmailer finds in the homosexual an easy victim. The late Lord Jowitt estimated that 95 per cent. of blackmail cases had a homosexual origin. It cannot be good for society that we should continue to enforce a law which creates a minority of men who are so vulnerable to pressure of this kind, and who, contrary to a widespread belief, have no assurance that if they report a blackmailer they will not themselves be prosecuted. The difficulty of obtaining proof in homosexual cases causes voluntary statements and admissions by accomplices to be relied on to an extent which is causing grave concern to legal authorities, and inevitably leads to the use by policemen of traps and decoy methods which are revolting to decent people.

" ' The Wolfenden Committee studied the evidence for three years, and recommended that homosexual behaviour **between consenting adults in private** should no longer be a criminal offence. This recommendation, except that it fixes the age of consent at twenty-one (which some of us would regard as unrealistically high), would put homosexual behaviour between men on the same footing as heterosexual or female homosexual behaviour.

" ' It has the backing of the Archbishops of Canterbury and York, the Church Assembly, the Church of England Moral Welfare Council, the Roman Catholic Advisory Committee on Prostitution and Homosexual Offences, the Methodist Conference, leaders of the Church of Scotland and the Free Churches, and the overwhelming majority of those who, in the course of their work, have to advise on problems connected with homosexuality.

" ' When this recommendation is implemented, it will at last be possible to tackle the problem constructively. No one knows what are the causes of the condition, and no one is likely to know while the only homosexuals who are willing to give information are those who seek psychological help because they are involved in a criminal case.

" ' It seems probable that upbringing has a large part to play, but guidance for parents is not easy while the whole subject is invested with an aura of guilt and secrecy. Yet the Government shows no sign of introducing the suggested legislation, and there is no evidence of a decrease in the number of prosecutions of consenting adults.   Arrests and sentences are more haphazard than ever, since some authorities and judges favour reform while others oppose it.

" ' In these circumstances it is not surprising that the problem is, if anything, growing worse. Uninformed discussion and flippant references to the subject are rife among the general public, and homosexuals themselves are less certain of their position than ever before. It is neither desirable nor possible to go back to the time when they were universally condemned; yet if they try to take the place in society to which they have a right, without resorting to secrecy and deceit, they are still in grave danger of criminal proceedings.

" ' To continue to enforce a law which has incurred widespread disapproval can easily give rise to a contempt for the law as a whole.

" ' Politicians are understandably cautious when asked to support a reform which might antagonise the diehards in their constituency parties . . . But homosexuality is a problem which cannot be shelved indefinitely.

" ' It calls above all for clear, dispassionate and constructive thought, and can only be aggravated while the official attitude remains repressive and negative. Legislation along the lines suggested by the Wolfenden Committee must come in time, and the situation will grow worse unless it comes soon '.

" At last came the day ", recorded Juliet's brother, " when my sister, as I had now grown used to calling her, was ready to leave the Clinic.

" As visualised—she had the great joy and happiness of walking down the steps of the Clinic wearing her dazzling white dress —arm in arm with me—and with Sandra following close behind. The sun shone brilliantly.   Juliet looked radiant, her dark hair blowing in a playful breeze—her dress flaring provocatively ".

PART FIVE

THE FINAL YEARS

1

FIRST FLUSH OF SUCCESS

" Juliet ", wrote her brother of that triumphant moment when she first stepped into the sunshine on the steps of the Clinic, " radiated personality, self-confidence and sex-appeal as she posed for the battery of cameras grouped outside the Clinic and stopped to answer the myriad questions shot at her from all sides by reporters of practically every known newspaper and periodical in the world.

" Everyone seemed incredulous. That this tall, striking, dark-haired girl with the breath-taking figure had once been a man seemed fantastic. Eagerly the reporters and Casablancians waited for her to speak— hoping her voice would betray her inner masculine elements. But, as she replied to their questions—her voice was immediately soft and feminine with only a tantalising hint of huskiness.

" Sandra followed close behind—eager to let Juliet have the cameras to herself—to be the central figure in this scene. Juliet hung on to my arm while she chatted gaily to the crowds.

" At last we found our way to the car that was to take us to the airport and home to England. Turning round, we waved to the specialist, the doctors and the dark nurse who were standing watching our departure from the top of the steps. They waved in reply as we turned to get into the car.

" Then the Casablancian countryside was speeding past the windows and the airport was in sight. I had booked our reservations in advance and, of course, the press had got to hear of it and were there in force also. Once again there was a battle to get

176

through them and the airport visitors, many of whom were English people on holiday. Finally—we made it to the plane and were safely inside. No international film star could have had a greater send-off than Juliet, that wonderful morning.

" Her eyes were glistening as she looked down—when we were in the air, at the sprawling white building of the Clinic, at the lush grounds surrounding them, where she had walked during her early periods of recovery. Then I saw her lift her eyes and look forward —forward to England and to the world which she felt sure now lay at her feet.

" At London Airport there were more reporters—who had been flashed news of our impending arrival from Casablanca. More pictures, more questions. In the Airport lounge we were surrounded by curious travellers, red-faced officials—and more photographers and newsmen.

" Juliet behaved magnificently. She looked fresh and vivacious the whole of the time. I worried a great deal about the strain after the operation and so many weeks of seclusion—but she didn't turn a hair. Now Sandra came in for attention—her striking beauty certainly not going unnoticed. TV cameras recorded the scenes for that evening's newscasts and interviewed Sandra, Juliet and myself on the spot.

" Home at the flat, we had to face yet another crowd of reporters and cameramen before we could get safely inside. Sandra had arranged for a temporary housekeeper during our absence. The whole place was spick and span, a meal laid on, the beds aired. There were piles of telegrams and letters awaiting us—the telephone rang incessantly from agents and impressarios after Juliet with contracts.

" We waited in that evening to see Juliet and ourselves on television. She looked wonderful. Her new-found femininity came over perfectly on the small screen. The camera did not betray her secret in any way. She looked what she was—a tall, strikingly beautiful girl.

" After that—we went to London's West End for supper and a late night show. Juliet chose the Golden Dome—scene of her triumphs before the operation. The management made a great fuss of us all and we had no trouble getting a good table in spite of the fact we had not phoned through any reservation. The other diners soon became aware of whom we were and we were the object of everyone's gaze. Juliet thoroughly enjoyed herself.

"It was delightful", continued her brother, "to see her—after the long months of anxiety—so young, vital and alive. I found a great protective spirit surging within me—so different from the old feelings of jealousy and infatuation. Sandra, too, smiled indulgently at Juliet and I could see a great fondness for her in her eyes.

"Many young men and older men, too, skirted curiously around Juliet, afraid to speak to her—conscious of the fact she was really of their sex—but too fascinated to disallow her altogether. I saw many homosexuals casting glances in her direction, some with desire in their eyes—others whose faces registered obvious jealousy. Juliet smiled at the men milling around her at a respectable distance. She looked, also, at the many women who shot angry glances in her direction—at the mincing, nylon-clad, short-skirted cigarette girls who seemed unable to keep their eyes off her.

"The atmosphere in the Golden Dome that night and in the early hours of the next morning was electric. A strange mixture of amazement, disbelief and hatred. The women, especially, emanated spite and malice towards Juliet by look and innuendo—as if they hated the invasion of their sex.

"To all this, however, Juliet acted with cool, calm confidence. Not once did she lose her poise or self-esteem. Indeed—she carried the occasion before her and, by her personality, her voice, her smile—became the centre of interest and the envy and admiration of everyone. The manager asked me if Juliet would go on to the band-stand and sing one of the numbers she sang before, when she first appeared at the Club. Deference to the agent and management of the new night club with whom Juliet had already signed a contract, however, forbade this.

"The next morning", continued Juliet's brother, "the papers published many photographs of our arrival at the Airport and outside our Town flat. Several columns ran various reporters' stories of the trip back to England. We ordered every paper, magazine and Continental and American periodical possible so that, over the following weeks, we would be able to see how Juliet's amazing story had been flashed and syndicated throughout the world. The Sunday newspaper medical correspondent called to write-up the Casablanca Clinic story for the following Sunday's edition.

" The following weeks before Juliet started rehearsals with the Midnite Spot—the West End night club with whom she had signed a contract—I was able to study Juliet's attitude towards Sandra. I noted a marked disinclination on Juliet's part to be alone with Sandra—as had always been so very much the case in the past.

" Sandra was quick to notice this and, I am afraid, was taking it rather badly.

" She had, I think, cherished ideas of a firmer link with Juliet than ever before, but Juliet, whose feminine mental make-up was now beginning to assert itself, was veering away from Sandra; away, in fact, from the female sex altogether, and was beginning to evince an interest in men. Which was perfectly natural if the body-mind relationship in Juliet's new personality was going to function in the right direction. Doubtless Sandra had foreseen this change of attitude but had not anticipated it happening quite so soon.

" On our various outings to clubs, restaurants, night clubs and theatres, Juliet was very much for the men. Now she did not smile and shrug them off as she had done that first night at the Golden Dome. She deliberately encouraged them with her smiles and conversation. We moved, now, among people who did not realise who Juliet was. She was accepted as a girl without any trimmings. Consequently—she found it possible and desirable to cultivate the attentions of men who wanted to meet her. Naturally, Sandra and I could not refuse such invitations. Very soon, Juliet had a whole host of men friends calling on her, phoning and writing her.

" Then came the time when she started wanting to go out with these men by herself. This, also, was something we could not refuse her in her new-found happiness.

" But it began to have a profound effect on Sandra. She grew thinner and began to lose interest in her appearance. I did all I could to make her feel happier.

" But I knew I was playing a losing game.

" The time had come in the lives of the three of us when Juliet was becoming an independent person—no longer reliant upon either Sandra or myself for constant companionship and support.

" But, as I reasoned, with Sandra—what was the use of us all having gone through such dreadful things in the past if now we were to try to deny the very thing for which Juliet had lived all her short life—the glory of being a ravishing female with all the excitement and glamour that goes with it—especially that of the inevitable and longed-for pursuit by the male ?

" It was not easy to reconcile Sandra to this situation. I felt very sorry for her.

" That she still loved Juliet there was no doubt. In fact—it was obvious she loved her far more now than ever before. A lot of that, however, was rooted in sudden jealousy of Juliet's wonderful looks and body to which Sandra could not now reach out—or share with her ".

2

JULIET'S FIRST LOVE AFFAIRE

Among the many papers that Juliet's brother lodged with the Clinic after Juliet's death were accounts of Juliet's affaires with men after the operation. In particular, Juliet's first love affaire as a woman was of obvious clinical interest and it is here reproduced in full :

" Now ", wrote Juliet, " I look at men in an entirely new light. Before the operation I was, more or less, neutrally inclined towards them—looking at them with neither the eyes of a homosexual nor with those of a woman. Now—thank heavens, I can appreciate them as a woman appreciates men.

" Poor Sandra ! In spite of the fact I still think the world of her, there is now a wall that stands between us, though she finds this difficult to accept. I look back with a certain distaste at the things we did together and wonder how those things could ever have been. But, of course, in those days, I was indeterminate and I see now, so well, that I was, in actual fact, loving myself through Sandra. She was the image and the likeness I most desired to see in myself. The time has come when I no longer need Sandra as a mirror, for I am a woman in my own right at last.

" I have met a man called Michael. He does not know about me. In spite of all the newspaper publicity and the photographs, and my nightly appearance at the Midnite Spot—he just accepts me as Juliet and believes me to be wholly and completely feminine. He is an artist and lives and works in a tumble–down cottage in the depths of the Surrey countryside. Seldom, if ever, does he go to town and only knows I appear at the Midnite Spot because he sees my name in the advertisements in the evening papers. He is so at one with his painting, for which he is quite famous, that he knows little and cares less for the sophisticated world just round the corner.

181

" He specialises in portraits. I met him at a country inn not far from his cottage when I went there one evening I had begged off from the night club. My brother had to leave for Town by himself because Michael asked me back to his cottage. My brother left me resignedly—knowing the time had come for me to start shaping a different outlook on life.

" Michael insisted on painting me—full length—in the nude. The first time there were only preliminary sketches, of course, but these were enough to make good excuse to see him again.

" Altogether—there were six sittings extended over a period of six week-ends. By the time the work was finished I was very much in love with Michael.

" He was tall, with auburn hair, good-looking, dressed atrociously in jeans and sweaters, but hugely talented. Many famous people had sat for him for their portraits. He was a gentle man. With him—I experienced the happiness of the female with the male for the very first time. He was an accomplished lover— sophisticated and kind. All that the specialist at the Clinic had promised me came true. I knew all the pleasures of the feminine sex and this was due to a perfect fusion of my mind and my body. I was completely able to thrust into the background my masculine beginnings and suffered no subconscious qualms or misgivings.

" For one whole year—my association with Michael was as ideal as any man-woman relationship could possibly be. The amount of time I spent with him at the cottage lengthened from week-ends to weeks at a time. Sandra I neglected completely. Of my brother I saw very little. They both appeared resigned to this natural turn of events, but I felt sorry for deserting them after all they had done for me and been through on my behalf.

" But I could not deny the natural, feminine urges within me. After all, this was precisely the reason why I had wanted to change my sex, so that I could enjoy life as a woman. I know Sandra was taking it all very badly, and I felt desperately sorry to have to let her down. But I could no longer look upon her in the same way. Now I realised that my love for Sandra had been a masculine love in spite of the fact I envied and admired her feminine state when I myself was still indeterminate. Now—and as it should be—I found thought of physical contact with her to be all wrong.

" All the time I spent with Michael, however, was not entirely happy. For one thing—I had to do all I could, all of the time, to prevent Michael wanting to go up to London with me. For I felt sure that, once in Town, I would be bound to be recognised as Juliet by someone or other who knew my history.

" For all these long months, I had been able to hide the truth from him. So great was my transformation and so complete was my enjoyment of, and capacity for, the female role, that Michael had no suspicion whatsoever that I had once been a man.

" By now he was the whole world to me. The very thing I had dreamed of had happened—I had fallen in love with a man. It was the fulfilment of all my dreams.

" Soon—the sessions at the Midnite Spot began to pall on me. The contract was for six months. It had been renewed for a further three months but, quite suddenly, one day, I decided not to go on with it and asked to be released from the contract.

" After some legal tussling—this was done—but I lost quite a few hundred pounds out of court in order to get the release.

" All the time I had had to be leaving Michael to journey up to Town in my car and back again in the early hours of the morning I had been undergoing a great strain. Added to that was the ever-present fear that Michael might—one night—decide to come to the night club and see me for what I really was.

" As far as he was concerned—I was a night club entertainer and his out-of-touchness with London life had prevented him from knowing the true facts. So, with great relief, I retired from the club and spent all of my time at the cottage with him.

" He painted several more studies of me in the nude, draped, and also did two portraits. Then came the day when he said he wanted to exhibit three of the nudes and two of the portraits in the Pemberton Galleries, Old Bond Street.

" This, of course, was something of a shock. I pleaded with him to drop the project; but the more I did so, the more keen he became. He wanted the whole of London to see me at the Galleries. Unbeknown to me—he went to Town to see his Agent and, in next to no time, had arranged an Exhibition of his works which included the three nudes and two portraits of myself.

" For weeks on end before the pre-view of the exhibition, I wrestled within myself as to whether to tell him the truth or not. But I could not get myself to do so. Each time he took me in his arms, each night we spent together, made him more vital and important to me.

"So I said nothing. And the day for the pre-view, and the opening day for the public came nearer and nearer. I confided my fears to my brother and to Sandra. But there was nothing either of them could do.

"I felt there was a note of triumph in Sandra's voice and a look of hope in her eyes as I explained the situation to them. Perhaps Sandra foresaw the break between Michael and myself when he learnt the truth and hoped I would return to her.

"That the nudes and the portraits of me would be recognised, first by the press and then by the public, seemed inevitable. The paintings were wonderful studies—absolutely true to life. As like me as any photographs could ever be. It did not seem possible that, during the arranged two weeks of the exhibition—there would not be at least one person who would recognise me—and tell Michael who I was and all about me.

"'Why do you **have** to fall in love?' asked Sandra. 'You can surely enjoy life without getting emotionally involved? Why can't things be like they used to be—just the three of us getting as much out of life as possible?'

"'What **did** we get out of life?' I asked. 'I led a hell on earth wanting to be a woman. My brother sacrificed an awful lot of happiness in life because of my problems; and you—Sandra— were you ever **really** happy?'

"'I was helping you', she replied. 'And I was happy helping your brother to help you. Ours was a life apart. We were all doing something. Now that it's done there doesn't seem much left. But if we were still all three together—and you weren't pursuing this fantasy of falling in love—there would still be lots of happiness in life that we could, all three of us, share'.

"'I can't help the way I feel about Michael', I replied.

"'But you **can**', protested Sandra. 'You are deliberately doing what all females **have** to do. But women fall in love to get married, to have a home and, above all, to have children. **You** can never have a child. You can never ever, really and truly, have a proper married life. You would be living under a cloud always. Afraid your husband might find out the truth about you.

"'And', she went on, 'supposing you told your husband the truth—perhaps before you got married—how long do you think the illusion would last? Don't you think that, when the sexy novelty had worn off—your husband would suddenly come to his senses and realise he was, in fact, sleeping and living with a **man** ? You would have to marry either a confirmed pervert or a terribly simple soul who would stick to you from sympathy rather than from anything else.

" ' Why ruin everything, Juliet ? ' she pleaded. ' Look at the way you have stopped being in show business. You were making a mint of money. In a year or so—you could be fabulously rich, invest your money wisely and have a hell of a life. You belong to the public, Juliet, not to some potty artist in a wreck of a cottage in the country '.

" ' Juliet ', said my brother to Sandra during this rather unpleasant scene, ' is following the normal female pattern of life. It could have been that, in spite of the operation, Juliet would have continued to think emotionally as a man and would have centred her physical desires on women—you, for instance, Sandra.

" ' But the mental change-over has been so very successful, and the feminine outlook which was there already, in any case, has been so strong, and **is** so strong, that Juliet is behaving precisely like a female.

" ' She falls in love.

" ' She will fall in love again.

" ' Michael won't be the first or the last. And—true to her gender—she will be willing to sacrifice everything to get what she feels she wants out of life—the love of a man. Are you so unsophisticated, after all, Sandra, to not be able to realise and to accept those facts ? '

" ' I do without men ', said Sandra. ' Why can't Juliet do without them as well ? '

" ' Because you are a normal woman with abnormal thinking processes ', replied my brother, ' and Juliet is an abnormal woman with normal thinking processes. Between the two of you, we have the wrong minds in the right bodies—or the wrong bodies for the right minds '.

" ' What about **you,** then ?' demanded Sandra. ' Are **you** a classic example of a right mind in a right body ? Do **you** fall in **love** normally, with normal women ? You do **not.** You don't even show a streak of emotionalism in you by being homosexually inclined. You're just a cold fish. How **can** you live that way ? '

" ' You can't expect Juliet to live that way, can you ? ' said my brother.

" ' Juliet is different ', said Sandra. ' Falling in love for Juliet is a dangerous business '.

" ' But for me . . . ? "

" ' At least it's rational ', said Sandra.

" ' And for you . . . ? ' my brother asked Sandra.

" ' I don't fall in love ', she said. ' I experiment with emotions and feelings and explore the physical experiences that these emotions produce '.

" ' But you were in love with Juliet when she was a man ? '

" ' Not in love ', replied Sandra. ' I was fascinated with the emotional and physical phenomenon that was Julian and Juliet —all in one '.

" ' You still **are** in love with Juliet ? ' persisted my brother.

" ' With the phenomenon that is Juliet ', said Sandra. ' And I don't want that phenomenon to collapse into a prosaic, conventional man-woman relationship. That, I feel, would be far too small for Juliet. To have suffered so much for so long, just to get married and to live conventionally ever after would be an anticlimax.

" ' Besides—what about public opinion ? The public have accepted Juliet as a man-turned-into-a-woman and have acclaimed her. So long as she remains single, they will continue to accept her until, inevitably, she disappears from view. But—until that time arrives, Juliet belongs to the public who have accepted her and made her. If Juliet marries—she will immediately become the centre of malicious gossip and unsavoury jokes. The public is too simple-minded to accept a marriage between a person like Juliet and a normal man. They might accept it, but they would never understand it. They would never flock to see her at clubs or in shows again. At least—the British public wouldn't. She would fade into premature obscurity.

" ' Juliet ', went on Sandra, ' lives and thrives on adulation and the opportunity to show herself off. Once she becomes the property of one man, all that would have to end ',

" ' I think ', I said, ' that you are misjudging me, Sandra. It is not so much the erotic side of married life as a woman that attracts me as the security of it. I do not mean financial security, but emotional security. The knowledge that I am wanted by one man. That I mean the whole world to one man '.

" ' You are being a **woman** ', said Sandra angrily.

" ' That is exactly why I went through that terrible operation ', I replied.

" That conversation took place before the pre-view day of Michael's exhibition. It was the first angry scene that had ever taken place between the three of us.

" A sudden chill went through me as I thought of the future that lay before me. Of constant discovery if I mixed with a lot of men. If Michael was destined to learn the truth and to leave me. Of my growing old and losing my looks and femininity. Perhaps reverting physically, in some terribly revolting way—to masculinity again.

" The next day I steeled myself to go, with Michael, to the pre-view ".

3

SOCIETY WELCOMES JULIET

" When Michael and I reached the Galleries ", went on Juliet's account, " the place was already filling up. Michael's paintings always drew a large crowd and this pre-view was no exception.

" He had some hundred and fifty canvases on show—including the nudes and portraits of me. Unbeknown to me—and, as a surprise, no doubt—Michael had arranged for the nudes and the portraits to form the centre-piece of the exhibition. As soon as I stepped into the Galleries, I could see them on the centre wall— with a special arrangement of blue drapes behind them and a battery of floodlights picking them out in front. They were certainly breath-taking. Audacious—compelling—electric.

" This focal-point of the exhibition was drawing the crowds. Already there were many gathered in front of the pictures and, as Michael forced me to approach the people, they drew aside to allow us to go through. Voices from all sides called to Michael. He acknowledged their greeting with a smile and a wave.

" Then the moment arrived when the audience—looking at the pictures in this particular group, looking at Michael and look- ing at me— realised that I was the subject of the paintings. An audible gasp went up as they took in the situation, then an appreciative murmur broke out. The catalogue announced all the studies of me as being just—' Juliet '.

" Looking back over the heads of the crowd—I was enor- mously relieved to see Sandra and my brother over by the entrance. I excused myself from Michael and, forcing a way through the crowd, went towards them.

" ' They've recognised me ', I managed to whisper.

" Sandra and my brother looked towards the blue drapes and the glow of white lights.

" But the crowd were not content to let me ascape as easily

as that. They turned round and were looking at the three of us. I could see Michael, head and shoulders above them—staring over at me. Then I saw a youngish fellow speaking to Michael and pointing towards me.

" I turned and pushed open the swing doors. ' Get me away from this place ', I pleaded with my brother.

" The next moment we were all outside. Sandra and my brother hustled me into their car. We drove round the streets until we came to a pub. Over drinks we talked.

" ' We're not **sure** ', said Sandra, ' that that young fellow **was** telling Michael who you were '.

" ' I know he was ', I replied.

" ' Does it **really** matter so very much ? ' asked Sandra crossly.

" We all went back to the flat after the drinks and, soon after we had got in—the door-bell rang. My brother answered it and there stood Michael. We asked him in.

" Michael managed to be perfectly polite about it all. I could see his eyes were steely cold as he looked at me. When he spoke to me his voice was just as cold. He did not say harsh things. If he had, I might have felt better. His coldness and aloofness struck a chill deep into me.

" After a few polite remarks to Sandra and my brother—he left. The very next day—the first day for public viewing—my brother went back to the Galleries to try to talk to Michael. But he was not there.

" Neither were any of the paintings of me. The blue-draped, floodlit centre wall was occupied by some abstract landscapes Michael had painted long before he met me.

" The press ran quite a few paragraphs that morning about the pre-view and all made great mention of the paintings of me— and once again the names of Julian and Juliet were publicised.

" Strangely—that was the beginning of my break-through into the society life of the West End. The exhibition lasted for three weeks and although my pictures were not on show—the press publicity brought me back again to the public.

" Invitations began to pour in from all sides and Sandra, my brother and myself were fêted right, left and centre.

" Photographs of our nightly doings in Town appeared in the newspapers and glossy magazines and I was, at once, raised far above the night-club level of previous days. Then followed private invitations by big property owners, theatrical ' angels ', Lord this and Lord that, and I was completely ' in ' with the Establishment.

" There followed hectic week-ends on yachts, at private house parties, days at the races and many trips abroad. Sandra and my brother were onlookers at these escapades. They seemed rooted together with the one bond between them being that of watching my headlong flight through life.

" Sometimes I had the distinct impression they were just waiting for the day to come when I would no longer be riding on the crest of this wave—as if they felt that something pretty cruel was in store for me.

" I fell in and out of love many times. Nothing was particularly intense on either side. Some of the men knew my secret. To others it was an unopened book. But, somehow in the end, they always found out about me. My face was so well known that, even though I gave myself many new names to suit the occasion— someone eventually knew me as Juliet and the man with whom I was having an affaire gave me up.

" This was something that hurt and puzzled me considerably.

" I had all that a woman could possibly offer. I was warm, affectionate, sophisticated. Well-practised in love-making since I knew the man's side so well—as well as the woman's.

" I suppose it was because I never had affaires with any kinky men. They were all wholesome insomuch as they were **men**—in the strictest sense of the word. When they discovered my secret— there was no revulsion. Only pity and wonderment. But the essential magic always vanished as soon as they realised I was not one hundred per cent. woman.

" I began, sadly, to wonder if I would ever discover the ideal relationship. If there would ever be any chance at all of keeping my secret to myself. Or if I would ever find a man who, discovering all about me, would and could love me even more because of it.

" But this seemed an impossibility.

" Perverts I avoided like the plague, though I could have had cash and care lavished on me by many of them. But this, even as a thought, was revolting to me.

" All the publicity my case had aroused stood in the way of perfect peace of mind for me, of course. I was, indeed, public property almost everywhere I chose to go. And so many photographs of me were published in the papers and periodicals that I never had the slightest chance of escaping discovery.

"I made quite a few appearances in Continental night spots and twice I contracted to appear at Las Vegas. There was, for a time, a lot of thought and talk about my signing a film contract with a Continental film company to make a film of my life. A young boy film star was to be engaged to play me as a boy; an adolescent star, very much like the child, was picked to play me as a teenager. I, of course, would then have taken over to play myself for the rest of the film. The whole thing fell through because of feared censorship troubles that would prevent world-wide distribution of the film.

"However—for five solid years I lived the life of a queen. Each year I grew more mature—my feminine lines settled down and my voice had long since outgrown its initial huskiness.

"I kept in constant touch with my brother. Sandra started off by writing me a great deal. Her letters followed me all over the world. Always they were warm and wistful. There seemed an ever-present conviction that, one day, I would return to her—just as I had been before.

"Time—it seemed—stood still for Sandra.

"I kept all her letters and frequently replied to them. I also kept in touch with my brother. He told me in his letters that his Harley Street consultancy had grown considerably after my operation—that he was snowed under, almost constantly—with people wishing for a sex-change or, at least, relief from their transvestite and trans-sexual problems. I felt I was, in this remote way—repaying him for his years of devotion and attention to my particular problem.

"Then, one day, while I was in Mexico, my brother wrote to tell me that Sandra had disappeared. She had suddenly packed most of her important things, taken all her money out of her Bank —and vanished, without a forwarding address or any indication as to where she might have gone.

"I could do nothing but return to England, which I did the very next day.

"My brother seemed strangely alone in the flat when I first saw him again. Even though no real love had blossomed between him and Sandra—she had left her mark on him. She had stood for the one thing in common they had with each other—my development from a man into a woman.

"Now she was gone—and I was so well-launched on my wished-for future. My brother looked much older. Far more sad. I felt intensely sorry for him".

4

FEMALE FREEDOM

" My brother ", continued Juliet's account of his return to England after Sandra's disappearance, " gathered that Sandra had gone off on a voyage of Lesbian adventure to allay her hurt at my disappearance from her life.

" He could not accept that she had gone off with a man. She had left no note, written no letter. Had, in fact, disappeared into thin air.

" My brother spent hours contacting friends we both knew in an attempt to discover where she **had** gone—but all this was quite fruitless.

" Neither of us felt she had done anything of a suicidal nature —for, with all her complexes, Sandra was an incurable lover of life.

" In an attempt to try to understand and to analyse the psychology of Sandra, my brother spent many hours researching into text books and papers concerned with the psychology of the female.

" I went through a lot of stuff with him, and I made special note of these following short extracts from ' **Sexual Behaviour in the Human Female** ', published in 1953 by W. B. Saunders Company, of Philadelphia and London.

" This tremendously searching analysis of the female was a compilation of observations and data collected by such people as Alfred C. Kinsey, Wardell B. Pomeroy, Clyde E. Martin, and so on.

" The particular passages I noted dealt with what I looked upon as the exhibitionist flair in the man—suppressed by law if it got out of hand—and the relative freedom of the female to flaunt her Lesbian tendencies to the world.

" ' There is a widespread opinion which is held both by clinicians and the public at large, that homosexual responses and completed contacts occur among more females than males. This opinion is not borne out by our data, and it is not supported by previous studies which have been based on specific data.   This opinion may have originated in the fact that females are more openly affectionate than males in our culture.

" ' Women may hold hands in public, put arms about each other, publicly fondle and kiss each other, and openly express their admiration and affection for other females without being accused of homosexual interests, as men would be if they made such an open display of their interests in other men.

" ' Males, interpreting what they observe in terms of male psychology, are inclined to believe that the female behaviour reflects emotional interests that must develop sooner or later into overt sexual relationships. Nevertheless, our data indicate that a high proportion of this show of affection on the part of the female does not reflect any psychosexual interest, and rarely leads to overt homosexual activity.

" ' Not a few heterosexual males are erotically aroused in contemplating the possibilities of two females in a homosexual relation; and the opinion that females are involved in such relationships more frequently than males may represent wishful thinking on the part of such heterosexual males. Psychoanalysts may also see in it an attempt among males to justify or deny their own homosexual interests.

" ' The considerable amount of discussion and bantering which goes on among males in regard to their own sexual activities, the interest which many males show in their own genitalia and in the genitalia of other males, the amount of exhibitionistic display which so many males put on in locker rooms, in shower rooms, at swimming pools, and at informal swimming holes, the male's interest in photographs and drawings of genitalia and sexual action, in erotic fiction which describes male as well as female sexual prowess, and in toilet wall inscriptions portraying male genitalia and male genital functions, may reflect homosexual interests which are only infrequently found in female histories.

" ' The institutions which have developed around male homosexual interests includes cafés, taverns, night clubs, public baths, gymnasia, swimming pools, physical culture and more specifically homosexual magazines, and organised homosexual discussion groups; they rarely have any counterpart among females.

" ' Many of these male institutions, such as the homosexually oriented baths and gymnasia, are of ancient historic origin, but there do not seem to have been such institutions for females at any time in history. The street and institutionalised homosexual prostitution which is everywhere available for males, in all parts of the world, is rarely available for females, anywhere in the world. All of these differences between female and male homosexuality depend on basic psychosexual differences between the two sexes.

" ' Society may properly be concerned with the behaviour of its individual members when that behaviour affects the persons or property of other members of the social organisation, or the security of the whole group.

" ' For these reasons, practically all societies everywhere in the world attempt to control sexual relations which are secured through the use of force or undue intimidation, sexual relations which lead to unwanted prgenancies, and sexual activities which may disrupt or prevent marriages or otherwise threaten the existence of the social organisation itself.

" ' In various societies, however, and particularly in our own Judeo-Christian culture, still other types of sexual activity are condemned by religious codes, public opinion, and the law because they are contrary to the custom of the particular culture or because they are considered intrinsically sinful or wrong, and not because they do damage to other persons, their property, or the security of the total group.

" ' The social condemnation and legal penalties for any departure from the custom are often more severe than the penalties for material damage done to persons or to the social organisation.

" ' In the American culture there are no types of sexual activity which are as frequently condemned because they depart from the mores of the publicly pretended custom, as mouth-genital contacts and homosexual activities.

" ' There are practically no European groups, unless it be in England, and few if any cultures elsewhere in the world which have become as disturbed over male homosexuality as has the United States. Interestingly enough, there is much less public concern

over homosexual activities among females, and this is true in the
United States and in Europe and in still other parts of the world '.

" Searching through many belongings Sandra had left behind
her at the flat—we came across many photographs of myself as a
young boy, many she took at various stages of my change into a
female, and a whole bundle of letters I had written to her throughout the long years.

" It seemed as if Sandra had made up her mind to leave my
brother and me well behind—to thrust out of her life all and
everything that would remind her of us.   In her wardrobe were
many gowns left behind—and, tucked away in the recesses—the
very same short, white tennis skirt I had been wearing that long,
long time ago when Sandra had first seen me dressing up and had
discerned—in me—a kindred spirit. Suddenly—I was lonely for
Sandra—and felt an important influence in my life was suddenly
—unexplainably—missing ".

5

A LETTER FROM SANDRA

"Many months later", wrote Juliet, continuing his diary, "there came a letter at last, from Sandra. It was addressed to my brother. He and I had spent a lot of time together again since Sandra's disappearance.

"Once again, on my return to London", continued Juliet, "I was in great demand everywhere and my brother and I had a great time at the height of the Season. I made various guest appearances at clubs and night spots in Town but I didn't sign up any long-term contracts again. I had many affaires with men which my brother watched with a certain curious detachment. For himself—he drifted around with me when occasion demanded. Otherwise, he went on living the quiet life at the flat but working very hard, of course, at Harley Street every day.

"The letter from Sandra bore a French postmark, but did not give her address.

"'I often wonder', ran the letter, 'what you two thought about my melting into thin air so suddenly, like that. But there was really nothing I could do about it. Without Juliet—life seemed terribly empty. That must seem very rude to you—(my brother) but, as you know so well, we have, neither of us, ever been of much use to each other—either mentally, physically or spiritually. So I was sure you would not really miss me very much.

"'As for Juliet—it seemed her life was so full there was no room for me. I often read about her in the papers and the glossy magazines. Often see her smiling at me from some lovely photograph. Really—she is getting more beautiful all the time!

"'I suppose neither of you ever ran into the artist fellow—Michael—again, did you? He struck me as being a particularly precious sort of man. Far too prim for an artist!

" ' What am I doing ?   I think I can hear you both asking this.   Well—I am living with a delightful girl who is a fisher-woman's daughter.   She is uncouth, terribly lovely, very earthy and primitive.   But she recognised me—if you get what I mean—as soon as we met on the beach one day, here, just a month or so ago.   Until I met her and decided to stay here while it lasts—I had meandered all over Europe chasing peace of mind.   Not easy to find with one such as me !   This girl fulfils a great deal in me.   She cannot talk in a lively manner—so I do not have to waste time being intellectual with her.   Her parents are both as earthy as she.

" ' I shall tire of her one day—no doubt.   But, until then— she serves to make life tolerable for me.   There are plenty of hot young men here but I think they look upon me as some kind of witch !   I do not bother to dress-up much.   I wear old slacks and sweaters. do a bit of fishing with my uncouth lover girl.   I read a lot and go dancing.   With the young men, of course—while the girl, who can't dance to save her life—sits in the corner glowering at me !   There is a God-Almighty row after each night spent dancing.   But —in the morning, she is as pliable as ever again.

" ' Oh God !   This is a life.   And not at all as I had planned it.   I visualised a happy time with Juliet.   Me living for her and she for me—with you—dear brother—in between—like some guardian angel, or crummy ward of court or some such dreary, boring individual !

" ' Tell Juliet that whenever she wants me back again, I will be ready to come like a shot.   I still cannot believe that her trans-formation has been so complete as to put me right out of her mind and her life forever.   I know the day will come when she will need me very badly.

" ' There are a few effeminate young men here as well as the swarthy types.   The girlish ones amuse me.   They will never amount to anything.   There has never been anything quite so perfect as Juliet.   I think she is quite a miracle.   I hope she returns to you soon.   I think she is burning up all her resources far too fast.   I feel her flame will die-out suddenly.

" ' Sometimes I get the most dreadful premonitions about her. I see her lonely, quite deserted by everyone.   Suddenly growing nasty to look at.   All the feminine sheen and gloss draining away from her like grease off a guttering candle.

" ' In front of a mirror— some day—for instance—staring at

her reflection. Suddenly—the lovely face begins to melt away. The face of a man starts to show through. The ugly, dark blue of unshaven cheeks appears. The hair falls out and the eyes get bloodshot.

" ' As for her body—breasts begin a revolting sag. Rolls of fat appear on her stomach. Her thighs grow scraggy. The flesh round her neck loosens and sags. I see her staring into the mirror. Seeing this dreadful catastrophe taking place.

" ' Is it possible ? **Could** this be the end ? Could her man-hood re-assert itself suddenly—turning her into a travesty of man and woman, neither elements or sexes perfect again ? I try, but I cannot see Juliet living a long life, and still keeping her radiant beauty, her lovely, feminine body. I think the enemy within her—her masculine glands and organs inside her must—some day—try to force themselves to the surface again.

" ' If that ever happens—what is to become of her ?

" ' Can **you** imagine her alone in a room—scared to go out ? Frightened to face her friends ever again ? Locked away in the cold corners of her personal terror ?

" ' It seems to me that we ask altogether too much of nature to keep up the charade for ever. What a dreadful fear will grip her then—as she sees her youth and her beauty pouring away from her like slimy water—leaving a grotesque, male skeleton underneath.

" ' **Can** you imagine ? Or is that sort of thing completely beyond you ?

" ' Soon—Juliet will be thirty. The average woman, at thirty, begins to show time on her face. Her body begins to wilt just that little bit. Do you really think that Juliet—a man-made woman—will be able to preserve herself ? Surely the nasty little chemical secrets of her man's body will start to re-assert themselves ?

" ' I believe you yourself, many years ago—had similar thoughts about Juliet. Do you think the specialist knew—and all the doctors, and that dark-haired nurse at the Clinic ? Were they conscious of the fact they were just giving Juliet a few precious years of happiness before the final rot set in ?

" ' We have both seen so many old homosexualists, with their sagging cheeks and jowls. Their tired, watery eyes. Their heavy, sensual lips, and have seen the faded female behind the mask still trying to struggle through. If that sort of thing can happen to a man who has not had the sex-change—what might happen to Juliet, who has experienced everything possible ?

" ' What a dreary letter this is—and this is the first time I have written you since I disappeared ! I am sorry !

" ' Now—about **you**. I hope things go well with you. That you are in the best of health. No women—I suppose ? I don't think you **will** ever marry—will you ? I suppose that, if the worst **did** happen to Juliet—you would take her under your wing and hide her away in the flat for ever ?

" ' I often wonder will I ever see either of you again ? I know it is in my power to return any day I like. Right now I could get a car to the airport at Nice and be with you in the flat in a matter of hours.

" ' Why don't I come ? Because I could not bear to see Juliet again and to know that she has practically disowned me. That she would not be able to be the same warm human being towards me she once was.

" ' And I don't think I could bear to see her start to slip back. I cannot be sure that all will continue to be well for her for the rest of her life. And I would prefer to remember her as I saw her the very last time. So don't think too harshly of me if I choose to take the easy way out—and to remain away from the both of you for a long, long time.

" ' Possibly for ever.

" ' The little fisherwoman's slut who is blindly devoted to me is knocking at my bedroom door ! She goes around the house half naked all day when she is not out fishing ! She is small and dark, with an elfish face that never seems to grow up. But I love her, for she has saved me from complete desperation at the loss of Juliet. And—in some ways—she makes up for the loss of your companionship also.

" ' Perhaps you will hear from me again soon. I will not give my address, for I do not want you or Juliet coming out to me. Let time take its time and let us see how fate works things out for the three of us—you, me, and Juliet.

" ' Love from Sandra '."

6

THE BEGINNING OF THE LAST FIVE YEARS

" Shortly after getting Sandra's letter ", wrote Juliet's brother in his Clinic report, " it struck me forcibly that Juliet was now twenty-five.

" Sandra's remarks in her letter about the possibility of Juliet returning, in some way, to her pre-masculine state, rather horrified me. Little did any of us know, of course, that we were, in fact, beginning the last five years of Juliet's life. That we would, in fact, **never** know what the ravages of time and the tricks of nature might bring down upon her.

" Perhaps it was as well ", went on Juliet's brother, " sad though it was—that Juliet chose her own way out of life when she was thirty—and that she did not live on into her forties and fifties and longer.

" Juliet's reactions to Sandra's letter were not very startling. It was obvious she was far too wrapt up in her own life at that moment to spare a thought for what had been in the past. There was no trace of jealousy at the thought of Sandra living with the fisherwoman's daughter.

" Instead of showing annoyance, Juliet produced, from a bundle of letters she had had from Sandra from the old days— a wad of notes Sandra had given her to read during the early stages of their emotional contact with each other.

" The notes were from the American publication **Realife Guide** —and I divined Sandra had given them to Juliet to read when he was a boy in order to justify her (Sandra's) behaviour. They were certainly illuminating and deserve inclusion in this Clinical Report on Julian Griffiths ".

. . . notes from Homosexuality and Crimes against Nature,
by Morris Ploscowe (Realife Guide—U.S.A.)

" Homosexuality is the preference by an individual for a person of the same sex, rather than a person of the opposite sex, as a sexual companion.

" It is an anomaly which afflicts both men and women. It is encountered in persons in all walks of life and in all professions or occupations. It is not recognisable by physical signs alone. Effeminacy sometimes characterises the male homosexual and masculinity the female, but more often male and female homosexuals are indistinguishable in body structure, voice timbre, or general behaviour from ordinary heterosexual individuals.

" Homosexual activity may violate penal statutes. Under the designation of sodomy and crimes against nature, specific kinds of sexual behaviour usually indulged in by homosexuals are prohibited.

" However, such behaviour as fellatio, sodomy, and cunnilingus is not confined to homosexuals. It may also be indulged in by heterosexual individuals, both married and single.

" The law has considered sodomy, crimes against nature, and homosexual behaviour as serious perversions, the free choice of depraved individuals, the product of vicious desires rather than anomaly or disease.

" Moreover, modern judges and legislators, like their predecessors, have laboured under the impression that the proscribed forms of sexual behaviour are comparatively rare, that they are not indulged in by ordinary individuals, and their very abnormality requires their suppression.

" However, modern research has cast doubt upon these premises. In the first place, acts of sodomy and crimes against nature occur in widely different social situations, and these social situations must be understood before there can be any judgment with respect to the offence or the persons involved.

" Female homosexuality ", continued Morris Ploscowe, " has been studied much less intensively than male homosexuality, but it too is far more widespread than is generally realised.

" Havelock Ellis estimated that there was twice as much female homosexual activity as male.

"Katherine B. Davis studied twelve hundred unmarried college graduates who averaged thirty-seven years of age.

"Of this number, half had experienced intense emotional relations with other women and over three hundred, or one-fourth of the total, reported sexual activities with other women.

"Of one hundred married women studied by Hamilton, one-fourth admitted homosexual physical episodes.

"Of forty Lesbians studied by Henry, thirty-two admitted bisexual experience, but only eight of these women stated that they obtained any sexual satisfaction from men. The rest found such gratification only with women.

"Until late in the last century", said Morris Ploscowe, "the stock explanations for homosexuality and sodomistic practices were excessive masturbation or appetites jaded by normal means of sexual expression.

"But science today offers an explanation of homosexuality in terms of growth processes and the failure of the sexual impulse to develop normally.

"The crucial period is adolescence. Then boys and girls crystallise their interest in the opposite sex. Then they begin the experimentations which lead to the eventual choice of a mate. In adolescence, the boy who is homosexually inclined or the girl who has a leaning towards Lesbianism may discover an aversion for the other sex and the strong attraction of his own sex. They may be confirmed in these feelings if, as frequently happens, they become initiated into homosexual practices by experienced adults or even adolescents.

"Students of homosexuality disagree as to why the sex impulse fails to develop normally in certain individuals.

"Some believe that biological and constitutional factors predominate in the development of the homosexual.

"All persons are said to have within themselves characteristics and qualities of both sexes. In the normal individual, the process of growth and development pushes the characteristics and qualities of his own sex to the fore.

"But in the homosexual, either through congenital defect, hereditary taint, or endocrinological imbalance, the growth process is arrested and the individual remains with many of the characteristics and qualities of the opposite sex.

"Thus many an invert or homosexual male has traces of

physical as well as psychological effeminacy, the feminine carrying angle of the arm, a feminine body conformation, long legs, narrow hips, deficient hair on face, chest and back, a high pitched voice, a feminine distribution of pubic hair, small penis and testicles, an excess of fat on the shoulders, buttocks and the abdomen.

" In some cases the physical and mental differences between genuine homosexuals and normal human beings are so marked that some scientists like Hirschfeld regard the homosexual as an intersex, a third sex which is neither altogether masculine nor altogether feminine.

" Another scientist declared that homosexuality is nature's way of redressing the male-female balance, because he found that while there are normally 106 male births to every hundred female, among the siblings of male homosexuals the ratio was 121.1 to 100.

" Homosexuals themselves frequently express the conviction that they are an intermediate type between man and woman ".

" Shortly after Sandra's letter had arrived ", went on Juliet's brother, " Juliet suddenly began to grow restless.

" She was dating men right, left and centre. In fact, she seemed to be fast developing nymphomaniac tendencies far out of proportion to the average female. No doubt this was due to her over-exaggerated femininity, aggravated, as it was, by the masculine glands that still, of course, remained in her general make-up.

" All her affaires were with men who didn't know who she was, and she carried the masquerade off most successfully in every case.

" It seemed now as if she had developed an unquenchable thirst for emotional and sexual conquests and I began, for the very first time, to feel very worried for her. She kept late hours, slept till well on into mid-day, and smoked and drank far too much.

" Things came to a head when, one day, I returned from my rooms in Harley Street to find her gone. A brief note on the dining room table told me she had flown to New York with one of her rich boy friends.

" This was the beginning, indeed, of the last five years—for tragedy lay full ahead ".

7

JULIET SEES SANDRA AGAIN

" By some inexplicable trick of fate ", wrote Juliet's brother,
" Juliet's disappearance sparked off a series of events that were to
lead to her ultimate downfall.

" Among Juliet's belongings, after her death, I found an
account of her doings after she had so suddenly left me alone in
London. An unexplained series of coincidences led Juliet directly
to the little French fishing village where Sandra was living when
she wrote her one and only letter to me ', went on Juliet's brother.

" I insert here ", he continued, " the account of the events
from the day Juliet first saw Sandra again—in that French village
. . . "

" I travelled ", wrote Juliet, " across the English Channel to
Calais ". **(Not to New York, as her note to her brother had
deliberately stated).** " I travelled alone. Suddenly—I was whole-
heartedly sick and tired of men. I was weary inside and felt I had
explored every emotion worth exploring. My one thought was to
get away to some place where no one would recognise me. Where
I would not be plagued with the attentions of men. Where I might
rest-up and try to re-adjust myself.

" I landed at Calais on a fine morning. Before the day was
out I was in a smart hotel in Paris. At the reception desk the next
day I asked where I might find a secluded place—miles away from
everywhere—where I could find peace and quiet. I was recommended to visit V——, a small fishing village on the south coast
of France.

" The day after that, I booked out of the hotel and made my
way by train and coach down through France towards the south
coast. In a few days' time, taking the journey by easy stages, I
reached V——.

" It was indeed a small place, with a great expanse of open sea, one or two or three fishermen's huts scattered here and there —a church, an estaminet, a small pension and pale blue and pink cottages here and there. Hills in the background formed a natural wall, it seemed, from the rest of the world. Before me—the wide sea. Silver sands and gulls wheeling overhead.

" There was a small hall where, in the evenings, the villagers danced and drank.

" I spent the first evening indoors, looking out of my bedroom window at the sea—the blue Mediterranean. Spring was lengthening into summer. It was warm and the evenings light. I could hear music coming from the hall and, later, when it grew dark, I saw gay lights and couples arm-in-arm, drifting in and out of it. The hall was a meeting place for villagers from the surrounding districts.

" Just before I was about to start getting ready for bed, I saw two girls come out of the hall. They were arm-in-arm. They started to walk towards the small estaminet where I was staying. It was nearly dark, but the blue light of a hanging street lamp lit up the faces of the girls as they walked by under my window.

" To my amazement, I saw the taller of the two girls was Sandra.

" She was looking as lovely as ever—her hair shining copper in the blue lamplight. She wore a short white dress. Her arms were bare. One of them was linked through the arm of the other girl, who was dark and came up to Sandra's shoulder.

" The other girl was in black tights, leather boots and tight black sweater. They laughed and talked as I watched them pass by immediately beneath my window.

" They crossed the small street and mounted the steps of a three-storeyed white house on the far corner. I watched them disappear through the doorway.

" A minute or two later a light went on in a room overlooking the street, on the top floor. I gathered the house was a dwelling place for fisherfolk, as quite a few had been going in and out of the place during the evening.

" It was difficult to believe that Sandra was only a few yards distant—but there was no doubt about it. I went to bed a little while later with mixed feelings—but determined to make myself known to Sandra the next morning. I wondered, before I dropped off to sleep, exactly what she would say if she knew I was so very close to her again.

"I was up and dressed early the next day. The sun was already warm and I ran down to the beach for a bathe. I wore a black bikini.

"For a while I swam around and then I saw Sandra advancing down the sands towards the water's edge. She had on a slim one-piece bathing suit. She was alone.

"Deliberately I swam to the shore and rose out of the water, right in front of her, before she began to wade in.

"As I advanced towards her, I slowly took off my bathing cap and my hair cascaded round my shoulders.

"It is not easy to describe the look on Sandra's face. For a few moments she just stood and stared unbelievingly at me, unable to say a word.

"'Juliet . . . ?' she said, at length.

"I nodded.

"Sandra took hold of my arm and led me up the shore, away from the water's edge. 'Have you purposely come to find me?' she asked.

"'No', I said. 'This is a complete coincidence. I've just left my brother in London and come away to escape'.

"'Escape what?' Sandra asked.

"'Everything', I replied. 'Men. People who stare at me. People who look upon me as some kind of a freak. People who only want to know me because of what I have been, instead of what I am'.

"We both lay on the beach together as the sun grew warmer and warmer and higher in the heavens. We talked about what had gone before, of what I had been doing since last I left her, of her reasons for so suddenly disappearing.

"'What about the girl you were with last night?' I asked at length.

"'Jeanne?' asked Sandra. 'She's out helping her family to fish. Soon, she will be free and I will be meeting her on this beach'.

"'You are having an affaire with her?'

"Sandra nodded. 'Just to pass away time', she said.

"'No men . . . ?'

"'No men'.

" Sandra got up and stretched herself, and stood looking
down at me.

" ' You're still horribly lovely ', she said. ' And I can hardly
believe you are the Julian of years ago. Are you terribly happy ? '

" ' Happy to be a woman ', I replied. ' But very lonely at the
moment '.

" ' Then why not come back to me ? ' asked Sandra. ' I will
come away with you to wherever you want to go. I will leave
Jeanne in a flash. Why can't we make a start all over again—now
that, by some miracle, we have met each other again ? I promise
not to cling to you too much. Not to be jealous. Just to make you
happy '.

" I shook my head. ' You don't quite understand, Sandra,
do you ? ' I replied. ' I am not as I once was. I want only men
now. I want the fulfilment of womanhood '.

" ' But that kind of relationship is so empty and shallow ',
said Sandra. ' And men want you for one thing only. And, when
the novelty has worn off—they are away for fresh adventures. I
love you spiritually as well as physically. I can give you real,
honest-to-goodness love. There is nothing—but nothing—I would
not do for you, Juliet. I would never leave you again '.

" She sat down beside me again on the silver sands. ' I practically grew up with you ', she went on. ' I was in right at the very
beginning of your change into a woman. I practically nursed you
all through those awful years up to the operation—and after. How
you can possibly throw me away the way you have done is
beyond me. I consider I am part of you and that you are part of
me '.

" ' But I want to live as a woman ', I insisted.

" Sandra sighed. ' Then why are you here—escaping—running away from it all ? From men, for instance, who can help you
to live as a woman ? Don't you know what you **really** want out
of life ? "

" ' This is the anti-climax, I suppose. The inevitable law of
reversed effort ', I replied.

" Then Sandra grew serious.

" ' One day ', she said, ' you may be hag-ridden. You may
be ugly. Your body may go to seed. Something mean and nasty
and spiteful deep down inside of you might suddenly decide to
come to the surface. All your beauty might vanish and your body

grow ludicrous. You might develop a ghastly cancer out of all that you have had done to your body. You may become a man again, with all the active desires of a man, but without the physical properties to carry out your new-born masculine desires.

" ' Remember, Juliet—remember **this**—you are **still a man inside of you**. Nature won't and cannot forget that truth. You have no womb, no ovaries, no Fallopian tubes. You have not the hysteria-mechanism of the true female. You do not possess the genuine mamary glands of the female. Your breasts are forced from a man's chest. Your vagina is a maltreated phallus and its nerve-ends are subjected to movements and sensations completely alien to them. The hair on your head is stimulated growth and your intestines are confined within the narrow limits of a woman's waist. The functions of your excretory organs are unnatural and misplaced. However the world looks at you—you are an ersatz human being '.

" Sandra rolled over on to her back as she went on talking. Gulls wheeled overhead and the sun grew hotter in a hazy blue sky.

" ' Man ', she went on, ' has not yet found the secret of eternal youth. Men and women grow old and faded. Their skin sags, their faces grow lined, their stomachs bulge. Their flesh grows baggy and flaccid. Their hair begins to fall and their eyes grow dim and unseeing.

" ' Who are **you**—Juliet—to live forever in glorious womanhood when, in fact, womanhood does not belong to you ? And who are you to live forever in glorious manhood when, in fact, you have renounced manhood forever ? '

" ' Why say all these things to me ? ' I asked. ' When you encouraged me from the very start ? '

" ' Because ', replied Sandra, ' at the very beginning, I felt we would would always be together. For all our lives. That I would be able to grow old with you. That there would be only you and me and that I could be with you always. When disaster began to show through, we would be able to share it together. I cannot bear to think of you miles away somewhere—out of my reach—and some dreadful calamity overtakes you and I am not there to help you '.

" ' What makes you think a calamity **will** happen ? '

" ' This is too much of a miracle to last ', said Sandra. ' You

are altogether too perfect a transformation. Everything is completely against the precepts of human nature. Against God.
Against medical science. Against psychosomatic medicine. You
are like an earthy immaculate conception. Almost as if—as a
woman—you never had a father or a mother. In fact—now—at
this very moment—your father and mother, were they still alive—
would **not** have a child they could really call their very own '.

" 'You, too ', I said, ' will one day grow old and faded and
ugly '.

' But as a true woman grows old and faded and ugly ', said
Sandra. ' But how are we to know how a man-woman body and
mind, such as yours, will grow old ? '

" ' Does it really matter ? ' I asked.

" ' Live for today ', said Sandra. ' Have men wear your body
out until it is devoid of all sensation. Have them play on your
mind until it becomes wearied and disgusted.   Go through the
pangs and pains of fantasy pregnancy and have your breasts fill
with imaginary milk. Pull nylons up the length of your feminine
thighs and pull in your female waist . . . but think the thoughts
of the man that must, some day, assail you again. You cannot
kill the subconscious for ever. That is a part of you that will
never die.

" ' Already ', went on Sandra, ' you turn away from men
because you are tired of them.   You leave London and your
brother to escape it all. But you are not happy, because you are
all alone with your thoughts '.

" Sandra put her arms round me and rolled over on her
stomach in the sands so that she could look down at me.

" ' Stay with me ', she said. ' I will not wear you out physically or sicken you mentally. I will be content just to be with you
—all of the time '.

" ' But Jeanne . . . ? '

" ' Jeanne is just an earthy little tart I amuse myself with.
She attracts me physically, but I cannot talk to her. She has neither
polish nor sophistication. She is lithe, supple. She has a body
that twists as I embrace her and she dresses like a young boy in
black leather and tights. She is a little nymphomaniac and would
go with a man as much as with me. She adores me because I am
the first woman without the stink of fish in her hair who has paid
her any attention '.

" ' She will hate me ', I said.

" And—at that moment—Jeanne came swinging down the beach towards us both.

" Her black hair was almost down to her waist. Her face was pale. Deep-set eyes divided high cheekbones.

" She wore a very short, coarse black linen skirt well above her knees and a tight black sweater. She stopped right near us and I could see, as the sea breeze ruffled her skirt, she was naked underneath.

" She looked down at me and, in rapid French, asked who I was. Sandra replied in the same language and Jeanne squatted on her haunches to take a closer look at me.

" ' Ah—Juliet ', she said, after staring hard at me. She got up and, going round to Sandra, who was sitting up on the beach, sat down beside her and put her arms possessively round her waist.

" With a quick movement she threw Sandra on to her back and lay full length beside her.

" In front of me—and with a pout of triumph on her lips—she kissed Sandra full on the mouth.

" I ran down to the water and plunged in. Swinging strongly, I reached a rocky promontory and swam round it—out of sight of Sandra and Jeanne. I clambered out of the water and climbed up the jutting rock. From the top I could look down the other side.

" I saw Sandra and Jeanne locked in a close embrace.

" Sickened—I climbed down again and made my way back to my room ".

8

NIGHTMARE IN EUROPE

" I had plenty of money ", went on Juliet's account. " With some of it I bought a high powered car and sped away from that French village. Away from Sandra and the dark girl. Away from the sight of the two of them on those silver sands.

" Away from myself.

" One moment I was frantically jealous of Sandra and the dark girl. Another moment I didn't care a hang. I picked up some drugs from a quack who liked the look of my money.

" I sped on, in the car, into an infinity of long days and nights. Now I knew my life had reached a climax. Of men I had had enough. With them I was satiated. What else was there left in life ? What had everything been for ?

" To say I missed my brother was true. But to return to him would be defeat. To say I missed Sandra would be a contradiction of my new way of life.

" I sped aimlessly on through country lanes, through villages and hamlets, round mountains, by lovely lakes and up into blue misted hills, high above the sea.

" I hugged the Mediterranean coast for mile after mile.

" I spent the nights in a city here, in a town or village there. In a lonely farmstead with old people glad of the money and of my company.

" The weeks lengthened into months but still I kept on— working my way across those parts of Europe in which it was safe to travel.

" What I was searching for I did not know.

" Sometimes—I would amuse myself with some young man, resurrecting, for a brief spell, the old magic of love and desire. But it quickly palled and I disappeared into the night again.

" Sometimes I found myself looking back with longing for the secure days spent with Sandra and my brother. Days before the operation when there seemed everything in the world to which to look forward. But now—what would the future hold ? I inspected myself in a mirror in whatever hotel bedroom I was in, and each time I looked at my naked body, it seemed as perfect as ever.

"A few knowing men came my way who saw through my secret and knew me for what I was. They attempted clumsy love-making, and I hated them for their self-assurance, the way in which they flaunted their perverted masculinity, but treated me as a man also.

"I met a ' madame ' or two who ran brothels. They pleaded with me to join them as a very special ' line ' to offer elderly perverts. Sleazy night clubs were anxious to book me. A transvesti —on the Continent—is a popular act and I would have been well paid.

"All seemed to have suddenly gone wrong with my world. The adulation, the envy the admiration—all seemed empty and useless. I sought out a minister of the church and confessed to him my sins. But he had little to offer me by way of comfort.

"One day I awakened from a disturbed night's rest, weeping —and I could not stop all day. For many days I went around red-eyed, the slightest set-back causing me immeasurable hurt and anguish. I tried to seek entry to a monastery but they would not have me as I was not a proper man. A nunnery also, rejected me, for I was not a proper woman.

"Suddenly—I felt stateless. Inhuman. Not of this world at all. The company of perverts—which I could have had in plenty —appalled and revolted me. All I wished for was to live with, and to belong to, decent, normal people.

"I heard of a psychiatrist in Paris. I sped back across France —eager to see him. Breathless, I arrived one morning but I didn't have an appointment. I made one and went back and booked in at the same hotel at which I first stayed before I went to the village where I discovered Sandra.

"The next morning I set out to see the psychiatrist. He was a Frenchman, well versed in sexology, as most French medical and mind specialists are. Sex is an occupational disease with the French.

"At first I did not tell him I was a trans-sexualist. I settled myself on the couch, my short black skirt drawn up above my knees, which he viewed with obvious pleasure. A tight black sweater accentuated my bosom and this he also viewed with obvious interest.

"Then he began to shoot questions at me :

"'Age ?'

"'Twenty-six'.

"'Occupation ? '

"'Entertainer. Night clubs'.

"'Married ? '

"'No'.

"'Any love affaires ? '

"I raised my eyebrows at this. 'What you you think ? ' I asked.

"He shrugged his shoulders and put his head to one side.

"'We continue', he said. Notebook in hand, sitting beside the couch but just out of eye-range—he went on :

"'Illegitimate children ? '

"'Hardly', I said.

"'Sex ? ' he suddenly shot at me.

"I sat bolt upright on the couch.

"'Don't lie to me', he went on before I could reply. 'I know you are a transvesti'.

"'I don't fool you ? ' I asked, with a smile.

"'Non', he said. 'I can tell a transvesti a mile away. Now—undress—please'.

"'But you are a psychologist . . . ' I protested.

"'A psychiatrist', he corrected me. 'That means also a medical man. I have walked the wards. I understand the human body as well as the mind. Now—please—undress'.

"'I have had the operation', I said, as I slowly began to remove my clothes.

"'Ah !—a trans-sexualist ? '

"'I am Juliet Griffiths'.

"'The Juliet Griffiths ? '

"'There is only one', I said coldly.

"I removed my skirt and slip and bra and stood in my panties and suspender belt and black nylons.

"'And the rest', he said.

"Without a word, I loosened my suspenders, rolled my nylons

down my legs and stepped out of them. Then I pulled down the panties and undid the suspender belt.

" It dropped to the floor. I stood there naked.

" He looked me up and down.

" ' A wonderful specimen ', he said.

" He crossed the room, opened the door and called out to someone. The next minute his receptionist, a woman of about forty or so, came in. He indicated she should remain in the room.

" ' Is that really necessary ? ' I demanded.

" ' Professional etiquette ', he said. ' A practitioner must not be alone in his consulting room with a nude woman '.

" ' But you know I am a transvesti ', I said. He looked at his receptionist who, in turn, looked at me with renewed interest.

" ' Transvesti or not ', said the psychiatrist, ' it is still advisable to have a third party present.

" ' Now ', he went on briskly, ' Lie down again on the couch and we will continue '.

" He then carried out a quick and delicate examination of my lower regions. ' A wonderful operation ', he said. ' At Casablanca ? '

" I nodded.

" ' Doctor ——— ? ' he asked, mentioning the name of the specialist who had performed the operation.

" I nodded.

" ' You wish to be a man again ? ' he suddenly shot at me.

" ' No such thing '.

" ' You regret losing your manhood ? '

" ' No '.

" ' You long for a child ? '

" ' No '.

" ' You suffer from anti-climax ? There is now nothing more in life ? You have done it all ? There is nothing left ? '

" ' Something like that ', I replied

" He shrugged. ' You love men ? ' he asked.

" ' Yes '.

" ' Women ? '

" ' Once. But not now '.

" ' You enjoy full sexual satisfaction as a woman ? '

" I nodded.

" ' What **now** from life ? ' he asked. ' A husband ? A home ? '

" Before I began to answer he told me to get dressed again. As I did so, he wrote notes in his book. He motioned to his receptionist that she could now leave.

" She got up and went out of the room.

" When I was fully dressed again he told me to lie on the couch once more, and started to fire more questions at me.

" ' Any relatives ? '

" ' A brother. My parents are both dead '.

" ' You have the death-wish ? '

" I was perplexed for a moment.

" ' You mean ', I asked, ' am I tired of having to go on living ?'

" ' Precisely '.

" I pondered this.

" ' Sometimes ', I replied, ' I feel that life is not worth living any more '.

" ' You need a man to whom you can cling for the rest of your life ? '

" ' It **could** be that ', I said. ' But I cannot love any more '.

" ' But naturally ', he shrugged. ' You live the life of a man and you live the life of a woman. What can you expect ? A man loves in this way—a woman loves in that way. An in-between— loves like—**what** ? '

" He gestured with his hands.

" ' This is not **real** loving ', he went on. ' This is experimentation. There is no deep, true emotion here. You love only yourself. First—you love yourself as a man—as a narcissi. You love your masculinity and seek to show it off.

" ' Then you tire of this and want to be a passive woman. To receive instead of to give. You have money. Friends. It all helps. So—you have the phalloctomy and—voila—you are no longer a man but a woman ? But only outside '.

" He thumped his chest.

" ' Inside ', he went on, ' inside—you are still a man—no ?

" ' But of course. So now you wish for the strong, virile, masculine thrust that proclaims you as master of the female. But all you can now do is to lie still and the man is the attacker. Deep inside—you resent this because you are **really** still a man. You understand ? '

"He went on: 'It is a foolish, idle dream, this, of the man who wishes to be a woman'.

"'But you are supposed to **understand** that sort of thing', I protested. 'You are a mind doctor'.

"He gestured with his hands again.

"'But of course I am a mind doctor. And I know this man-woman wish as a very great sickness of the mind. As a dream that soon becomes a nightmare.

"'Now—you hover between the desires of a man and the desires of a woman. In bed—you cannot behave as a woman and enjoy sex as a woman enjoys sex, for your organs are not real. Most of it is of the mind. A great fantasy. A wishful thought. You persuade yourself you are a woman and enjoying a man as a woman enjoys a man. But—this is impossible.

"'And—now—you can no longer enjoy a woman as a man, for you have sacrificed that very thing that **makes** a man a man'.

"I got up from the couch in anger.

"'I came to you for help . . .', I said.

"'But I **do** help you', he replied. 'I show you to yourself for the first time. What else **can** I do? I cannot send you away and say: "enjoy yourself for you are truly a woman. Enjoy yourself for you are really a man"'.

"'I can only tell you the **truth**. By becoming a woman—you have destroyed your most cherished illusions of the desirability to be a woman. By sacrificing your manhood you have robbed yourself of the true function for which you were put on this earth',

"'But you do **not** understand', I protested. 'I was always tortured—from an early age—because I was a boy and not a girl'.

"He waved this away.

"'I know, I know', he said. 'I know all about you. Do you not think I followed your case with great interest? Do you not think I have every newspaper story about you—that I do not know all your history?

"'All the psychological and the medical world knows of you. There is nothing new you can tell to any of us.

"'But—I tell you the truth about yourself. You are alone now, and afraid. You take drugs to drive away fear. You drink. You sleep little. You drive up and down and round and round. Speed. Speed, speed all of the time. For now you run away from yourself. You have made a mistake—no?'

" ' Mistake ? '

" ' In having the operation. But no miracle can remove your breasts. Or give you back the symbol of a man '.

" ' I have made no mistake ', I replied.

" He shrugged.

" ' Then why are you here ? Why do you come to me ? For a headache ? For bad dreams ? '

" ' Because I want help ', I said.

" ' What help can I give to you ? Now—you have the body of a woman. You are beautiful to look at. Your breasts—magnifique ! Your waist and your hips—Oo la la !

" ' What more can we want ? Is this not the culmination of a life's ambition ? Have you not thrown back into your dead parents' faces the gift they gave to you ? The gift of manhood ? What is it to be a beautiful woman ? '

" ' I thought it would be everything '.

" ' Some women think it would be everything to be a strong, virile, handsome man. But surgery cannot give them man's sexual weapon or take their breasts away from them and give them beards.

" ' If you wished to be like a woman—why were you not content just to be a transvestite—a cross-dresser ? Here, on the Continent, transvestites are popular. They make a lot of money in the theatre. Then, as a transvestite—you could have satisfied your urge for femininity '.

" ' But—that was not enough ', I said. ' It all went far deeper than just the desire to dress up as a woman. I thought as a woman. I felt I had a woman's instincts. I wanted to be a woman through and through. Just dressing the part wasn't enough '.

" ' Think ', went on the psychiatrist, with cruel doggedness. ' Think what it would have meant if you had been content just to cross-dress by yourself, or with understanding friends, or on the stage. You could have had your moments of joy as a female but —when the urge overcame you to be a man—you could have behaved as a man. You could have had homosexual relationships as well as normal relations. Then—when the transvesti compulsion overcame you again—you could have satisfied that also. You would have had the best of three worlds '.

" ' It was deeper. It was deeper than all that ', I insisted.

" ' There was nothing carnal or sexual about it when it first began. I admired the female sex. I loved them for their beauty—their fragility. The way they walked and talked and behaved.

" ' I loved them for the thoughts they had. Their deep perception. The way in which they could appreciate the lovely things of life far better than a man.

" ' It was not only the sexual nature of the woman that I sought '.

" ' You wanted to give birth to a child as a woman ? '

" ' I wanted a child, yes. And I wanted to be able to love it as a mother loves her child '.

" ' But—surely ', said the psychiatrist, ' surely you knew that a trans-sexual operation would not make it possible for you to have a child of your own—produced from a womb ? '

" ' Yes ', I replied. ' I knew that, of course. But I felt that I could adopt a child and give it the love a woman would give to her very own child '.

" ' This would be impossible. No woman can love an adopted child as much as a child who has come from her own body. This is the law of nature. How could you hope to love a child that, first, had not come from your own body and, secondly, how could you love a child with a mind that was not really the true mind of a woman ? '

" ' I just hoped and prayed for all those things to happen to me '.

" ' I am sad for you ', he said. ' I have met many transvesti. I have met two, also who, like you, had the operation. But it was for carnal happiness alone. For success in show-business. But—I see—with you, it is very different. I would say you have been, in a way, dedicated to a cause that no other man has had thrust upon him. And now—you are alone and bewildered and frightened '.

" He thumbed through the notes he had been taking.

" ' What can I do for you ? ' he asked. ' I am a famous man. I have helped so many peope. I have written books. I have lectured. Your brother, also, is a psychiatrist ? '

" ' Yes '.

" ' And he cannot help you ? '

" ' He has done all he can. He helped me from my early days. He stood by me all the time. And a friend—a girl called Sandra —she also helped me all my life. But I have left them both '.

" ' Why is this ? '

" ' That—I cannot explain. I don't know. And I find I cannot go back to either of them. The girl Sandra, whom I think I once loved in a strange sort of way, is having an affaire with another girl '.

" ' Ah—a Lesbian ? '

" I nodded.

" ' And—you are jealous ? '

" ' Not jealous. Just revolted. I see no beauty in that sort of relationship '.

" ' And your brother ? Have you no regard for him ? '

" ' I love him as a brother. But that is not deep enough '.

" ' So ', said the psychiatrist, ' you have no one to love—and no one loves you ? '

" ' I suppose that is the case '.

" ' Very sad. For everyone must love someone. And everyone must have someone loving them. That is the way of the world. The unloved are unhappy, lonely people. Those who cannot love are even more unhappy and even more lonely.

" ' Mon dieu ! What can we do with you ? If you leave this consulting room—you will again go driving through the days and nights. Taking drugs to keep yourself going. Will you, perhaps ', he suggested, ' allow me to take you into my private Home for a little while ? I have just a few patients. They are very happy. Slowly, I am curing them of their various obsessions. None of them are serious cases. Suicidal tendencies. Manic depressives of a very mild order. Cases of melancholia. A heavy drinker who wishes to be cured by psychiatry. A drug addict or two '.

" ' But I am none of these things—none of these people ', I said. ' I am not a case '.

" He put his hand on my shoulder.

" ' But—my dear ', he said, ' you are a case. An exceptional case. You are in great need of care and protection. Think of the years ahead. Years to which you must become adjusted before it is too late.

" ' Can you say, with any strong conviction, that you will marry happily and settle down with a man who will accept you as a trans-sexualist and love you for it ? Or with a man upon whom you will be able to practise a life-long deception ?

" ' If you remain single—what is to become of you ? Soon,

your capacity for earning money as an entertainer will go. The public will lose interest in you. Managements will no longer wish to book you as a transvesti '.

" ' What do you suggest ? ' I asked him. ' If I did come to your Home for a while—what could you do for me ? '

" ' You could rest up ', he replied. ' We could stop your desire for drugs to make the days pass away quickly. We could stop you drinking so much. We could curb your insensate desire for speed. We could, perhaps, calm you down to such an extent that perhaps a career could be found for you. You could become a sedate human being with some situation in industry or something that would bring you in a livelihood and keep you in clothes and food and a decent roof over your head '.

" ' That would be such a waste of everything ', I said. ' Such a waste of the long, anxious years waiting for the operation. And such a waste of the operation itself in which I risked my life and my sanity '.

" ' Be thankful ', he said, ' that your life was spared. That you came out of it all with a sound mind. I have seen some unsuccessful cases of phalloctomy where the patient has lost all reason for the rest of his life. I have seen patients who have developed into a terrible fusion of nymphomania and satyriasis—in which their masculine and feminine sexual urges have reached fantasy proportions and they have lost all mental and physical peace of mind and body. At least—let us say for you that you are lovely to behold. That you are intelligent and aware. That you are sensitive and gifted '.

" ' But if I was to have an ordinary job, as you suggest ', I said ' all these things you say about me would be wasted '.

" ' You have had your fling. You have been fêted from one end of Europe to the other. You have made a small fortune. The whole world knows about you '.

" ' But it would be hard to retire—to disappear '.

" ' You have disappeared already ', he said. ' You have started to run away. You are alone in Paris. God knows where else you have been hiding yourself these past months or even years. If you are so eager to continue you public life, why have you not a manager who is looking after your affairs? Why have you not men and women around you—a secretary, a manager, a promoter,

an impressario, all of whom are directing your life and keeping
you in the public eye ? '

"Before I could answer—he was telling me :

" ' It is because you are running away from it all. Because
you have retired already. Now—you can no longer face up to life.
Drugs and drink help you on your way. But this is only synthetic
living. You no longer live with a clear mind '.

"He went over to a cabinet and produced a bottle of brandy
and two glasses. He brought them over to a table near the couch
and poured out two glasses. He handed one to me. We drank in
silence for a moment or so.

" ' I see ', he said, ' death for you '.

"To that I could say nothing.

" ' Let me take you in hand ', he said. ' And perhaps it will
not be too soon '.

"I left soon after. I declined his invitation to go into his
private Home. I went back to my room at the hotel. There, I
put on some recordings of my songs at the Golden Dome and the
Midnite Spot. I read through the many, many pages of the diary
I had been keeping all the long years. I thought of the day when
first Sandra had walked into my bedroom and I had been dressed
in the white tennis skirt. Of the first night my brother and I went
out with me wearing a wig and women's clothes. Of my first night
at the Golden Dome.

"In the morning, I decided, I would leave the hotel and travel
to Italy. I fell asleep at length, when the first pale blue of dawn
was spreading across the sky over the Seine.

"I slept till well after mid-day. Then I dressed after a bath,
paid my bill and headed my car south—to Italy ".

9

THE FINAL AFFAIRE

" Once in Rome—I quickly got caught up in ' la dolcé vita '. There was little hope of escaping it. And, truthfully—I did not exactly go out of my way to avoid it.

" Now began once again, months and months of late nights— early morning dances, late nights spent drugged in sleep and up again for the same hectic round a few hours later.

" Here I met Antonio who took me for a woman and had no doubts at all about it.

" He was a night club owner and billed me tops for a complete season.

" And here, also, by some strange coincidence, I once again ran into Michael who had deserted his painting for once and journeyed to Rome for a short holiday. We met one day, very much by accident, in the sunlit streets of Rome.

" He had seen my star-billing outside the night club owned by Antonio and recognised me as soon as we met.

" I asked him to swear to keep my secret—for here—in Rome —I was known as Rosette, at the club and among my many friends. Michael was good about it all. He assured me he would not say anything while he was in Rome—that my secret should remain with him.

" I still held a torch for him. And it burned brighter after we had met a few times unknown to Antonio. Michael would motor me down the Appian Way, deep into the mysterious countryside outside Rome and—on grassy banks—we would sit and talk for hours.

" He had quite got over his discovery of my true sex and had forgiven me my deception. He told me the pictures he had painted of me were on show in London at a small gallery in Cork Street, off Bond Street, and that he had high hopes of selling them all. He asked me to keep in touch with him so that I could get my percentage !

"Michael and I met many times after that when I was not with Antonio and entertaining at the club.

"Then the day came for Michael to leave for England. I was sad to see him go but the bond of affection between Antonio and myself was growing stronger each day. I knew that something really very big was developing between us.

"At last Michael was gone and I was able to give all my attention to Antonio.

"He was tall—a few inches taller than myself. Dark. And with those Italian good looks that are so disarming but which have such strength of character ".

Juliet's brother's notes intervened here in the general Clinical Dossier :

"It seemed, from quite a few letters I got from Juliet, that she was, for four whole years, in Rome " (he wrote) " happily in love, for the very first time—with this man Antonio who was extremely wealthy, owned a night club in Rome, and had many other fruitful investments as well.

"Juliet asked me to visit her and Antonio more than once during those years and I found him most likable and quite unsuspecting of Juliet's actual sex.

"Antonio had no parents which was, perhaps, just as well. There seemed no complications whatsoever. Everything was running smoothly. So smoothly, in fact, that I really began to think that Juliet's story was going to have a happy ending, after all.

"Even if " went on Juliet's brother's notes " even if Antonio **was** ultimately to find out the truth about Juliet—it seemed that, so great was their devotion to each other—the problem would be surmounted and would not make any difference to their relationship.

"It was, however, something else quite different that finally started Juliet on the downward trend that was, ultimately, to lead to her death by drowning in a lake in Cumberland ".

Juliet's notes now took up the thread of events again :
" Antonio and I made love often. In bed, in the depths of the

glorious Italian countryside.   In France in estaminets when on holiday. In Spain, where he opened a new night club, with me, as usual, top of the bill.

" I had had my hair dyed platinum, so that the risk of my being recognised as Juliet should be reduced as much as possible. It seemed to work as a charm, for nowhere was I recognised, by public or press. I later let it go back to its original dark colour— but that was when Antonio and I parted for ever.

" I kept frequent communication with my brother and often asked him if he had any further news of Sandra. But he always had to write and say that she never communicated with him again.

" One day—out of idle curiosity, Antonio and I went to that little French fishing village to try to find her.

" She had gone long since. We saw the little fishergirl with whom Sandra had lived—but she just shrugged and refused to give us any information. It seemed as if Sandra had vanished into thin air.

" My brother wrote to say he was completing a book about my case, that was to be compiled from the Clinical notes and my diaries and his own observations and asked me to keep him up-to-date with my doings. Which I did, of course, for I knew that a book on my life would have large sales and do a lot of good for my brother.

" Soon after Antonio and I returned to Rome again, I began to suffer slight pains in the pelvic region—especially after Antonio had made love to me.

" I did not think much about them and certainly did not mention them to Antonio. I wanted nothing to worry him. Nothing to spoil the first and only true love partnership I had ever been able to form during the whole of my life.

" But the pains began to grow worse—more especially when Antonio was close to me in bed. Finally, I felt I would have to go and see a specialist. I made an appointment with a very good man in Rome and, unbeknown to Antonio, visited him one day.

" I had to explain my case, and under complete secrecy, to reveal myself as Juliet Griffiths—the trans-sexualist.

" The specialist was most intrigued but appeared pleased to be able to handle my case. He knew everything about me, of course, as my case had been written-up as a special Paper for medical associations the world over.

" The doctor insisted I stay in hospital for observation for a week, and we had to tell Antonio that possible child-birth complications were suspected. Antonio insisted we become married immediately I left hospital.

" But the specialist shook his head at this news.

" ' My dear Juliet—you must **not** marry ', he said. ' This is a very sad case. We cannot lead Antonio Figaro on any longer. We must tell him the truth '.

" ' That I am a trans-sexualist ? '

" The doctor nodded.

" ' More—and far worse than that ', he answered.

" A chill ran through me.

" ' What is worse ? ' I asked

" The doctor looked down at me in my bed.

" He ran his fingers through my hair.

" ' You are ', he said, ' a classic example of the true trans-sexualist. You have been the most successful—one of the most successful—examples of this particular mental and physical aberration this generation has ever known '.

" ' Go on ', I said.

" He seemed to find it difficult to continue.

" ' Am I turning into—a complete man again ? ' I asked.

" He shook his head.

" ' That could never be with a trans-sexualist such as you ', he said. ' You would and could go on, for the rest of your life, looking, and feeling like a lovely woman. A perfect example of a man turned into woman '.

" ' Am I **not** to go on like that ? ' I asked.

" He turned and flicked through the pages of a sheaf of white paper on his desk.

" ' This ', he said, ' is a transcript of the Papers on your case —published for—and issued to—practically every doctor of note throughout the world.

" ' Perhaps ', he went on, ' I can make you understand if I read a short extract from the end of the Paper written by Professor Hirschnel Adrianoff—the Polish gynaecological specialist '.

" He turned to the papers in his hand and started to read :

" ' Professor Hirschnel, in his final analysis of your case ', read the doctor, ' stated that—" this case of trans-sexuality is almost unique in medical history in that the subject developed a perfect feminine voice, perfect breasts, beautifully shaped hips and waist, feminine thighs and all the external attributes of a perfect female.

" ' " But—as to the **internal** structure of the vagina which was fashioned from the layers of skin originally covering the penis— there is some doubt as to whether this living flesh would or could continue to function for a natural lifetime of the subject. Should the flesh began to atrophy . . . " ' here the doctor paused and looked at me and asked me if I wanted him to continue.

" I nodded.

" He referred back to the notes.

" ' " Should the flesh begin to atrophy after a number of years due to frictional irritation set-up by sexual intercourse and the fact that the nerve-ends were being subjected to a strain for which they were not originally intended . . . " ' he paused again and looked down at me on the bed.

" ' Please read on ', I said.

" ' " Should the flesh begin to atrophy ",' read on the doctor, ' " There would be a distinct danger of a cancerous growth of a malignant nature developing inside the artificially induced vaginal canal " '.

" For a moment the doctor was silent.

" Indeed—all around me was silent.   But in the distance I heard a church bell toll, heard a bird flutter outside the tiny window of my room, heard a train chugging away in the distance.

" At last I was able to get myself to speak.

" ' And—has that cancerous growth developed ? ' I asked.

" ' It is in a seriously advanced stage ', said the doctor.

" ' How serious ? '

" ' There is now present ', he said, ' a cancerous " nest "—a mass of cancer cells in your vagina. And we have discovered cancerin—a ptomain in your urinal discharge that also points to uterine cancer '.

" ' And that means . . . ? ' I asked.

" The doctor turned away from me and stood, staring down, out of the window.

" The same bird fluttered outside—but this time I could hear its wings fluttering away into the distance.

" I waited to see if the church bell would toll again . . . but all was silence ".

10

RETURN TO ENGLAND

" I little thought ", wrote Juliet's brother, " when I left Rome after having seen Juliet—that that would be the very last time I would set eyes on her alive. That the next time I would see her it would be her lifeless body I would be looking at—on the shores of a lake in Cumberland.

" All I have to remind me of Juliet's last months in this world is a letter she wrote me before she drowned herself ".

" My dear brother ", (wrote Juliet)
" When last we met in Rome I was happy, as you know, with Antonio and all seemed set fair for me to settle there with him. I saw Michael again in Rome when he came there for a holiday. I was able to make my peace with him and began to feel very happy.

" I am writing this letter in a small hotel in the Lake District, overlooking the deep, calm waters that I know are soon to receive my body. Do not hurry through this letter, brother, feeling that you can save me in time. That will be quite impossible. When you are reading this—I will be gone.

" Shortly after you left Rome and we had said goodbye, which was to be, I see now, for the very last time—I began to feel a pain in my pelvic region. This I ignored until it grew worse, and began to come between Antonio and myself. So I went to see a doctor.

" I was not destined, after all, to grow old and ugly. Perhaps to revert to a caricature of manhood again.

" I was not to see my face losing its beauty, my hair fading and falling, my body growing gross.

" Those fears of yours and Sandra's were unfounded, as it happens. But I shall never know, and neither will you or Sandra ever know—what **might** have happened to me had I gone on living until forty, fifty—or even into my seventies.

228

" The fact of the matter is that I have developed cancer.

" Seriously.   Incurably.

" The things the specialist did to my body, in all innocence no doubt, and with good and honest intentions to help—have turned against me at last. I suppose we played with nature a little too much. I suppose it was unfair to make such violent demands on the nature of things, although there have been successful cases in the past, as you know.

" The doctor told me it was a one-in-a-million chance that cancer **would** develop after an operation such as mine—but—there you are—I **was** that one in a million !

" A pity. For I felt that I had shown men who live in the twilight of indecision that there **is** hope, after all. That it **is** possible to be operated upon and to be all that one could possibly **wish** to be.

" If my condition now teaches the medical profession anything —then my time and suffering will not have been wasted. Or if my illness is a warning to other males not to tamper with nature, but to make the best of the worst—then, again, I shall not have suffered for nothing.

" The doctor in Rome insisted I went straight to hospital. But he could hold no hopes for me. He could only hope to drug away the increasing pain for a while. The cancer—he said—had got such a hold on me that it would spread violently within a year; but, in hospital, at least I would have as much comfort and alleviation from suffering as was humanly possible.

" But I could not go. He piled me high with drugs, most unethically, he said, and let me go my way. But I was sworn not to mention his name—not even to you, brother. For letting me go was unprofessional conduct. I assured him I would leave Antonio and never again consort with him.

" Poor Antonio ! I hope he did not contract anything terrible from me. I never even went to see him again after I left the doctor. I returned to the hotel—packed my stuff and was off, in my car.

" And—can you guess where I went to ?

" I went to try to find Sandra.

" I felt I **had** to see her just **once** again. So that is one reason why you have not heard from me now for such a long time. I have been all over Europe in my attempt to find her.

" You must wonder if I ever **did** find her ? And **I** wonder if

you know what I know about her ?

" I will assume you do not. So I will tell you. After months of motoring here, there and everywhere, suffering pain—pain that bigger and bigger doses of my drugs seemed never to dull away— I found out, from a small post office in Norway, that Sandra was in M——.

" I walked straight up to the house in which I was told she lived. A pretty place in the Norwegian manner, surrounded by trees and half-buried in a deep valley.

" I rang the bell and she answered the door.

" She seemed shocked at my appearance. I was much thinner than ever before. She noticed I walked slowly, my eyes were dark-ringed and I was very pale.

" All this she remarked upon.

" She asked me in.

" A lovely house, dear brother. Before I told her my troubles —I thought I would ask **her** how life was going with her. It seemed —very well. I wondered what kind of a girl it was she was in love with now.

" It was not a girl. It was a man.

" And Sandra was married to him. She had been married for about two months that very day.

" So what was the use of telling her what had happened to me ? She would not have been able to take me into her house to spend with her what time there was left for me.

" She was lovely, vivacious. A new kind of life seemed to have seeped into her. She looked at me in quite a different way.

" I never thought it possible for a girl with Sandra's kink to turn so completely. I asked her where her husband was. He was away doing an oil deal or something big like that. But she showed me a photograph of him. He was dark and well built, with a good, mannish face.

" I looked at her and saw that this, after all, had been her destiny all along. This was what was to be—but none of us knew it.

" And for me—I looked at myself in a mirror in her drawing room and knew that, all along, this was what was to happen to **me.**

" And you—brother ? What is to become of **you** ? Are you to marry some nice, womanish woman and settle down ?

" The three of us have reached the end of the saga.

" It started that day in my bedroom in our house—when the three of us saw—for the very first time—the natures of each one of us mirrored in the other.

" I was to be the man turned into woman. Sandra was to be a Lesbian—and you—I do believe you are doomed to celibacy, for I cannot really **quite** see you married.

" Perhaps you are so disgusted and revolted by the whole horrible business of sex and all its complications that you shudder away from it.

" I cannot blame you. Sex is a dreadful influence when it gets out of hand. As it has done with me. As it did with Sandra. But **she** seems to have found happiness at last.

" From mundane people like our poor, simple-minded, conservative parents, came you and me ! You—the mind searcher, the analyser. Me—the trans-sexualist and twilight one. I am glad both our parents are dead.

" Now, my very dear brother, I will end this letter, sign it and seal it.

" I will put it in a perfumed envelope and, tomorrow, when daylight begins to break over the lakes—I will go down a short, winding hill to a tiny little post office. Outside the post office is a little square letter-box fixed into the wall.

" All these long years that little red letter-box has been waiting—its mouth wide open—to receive this letter from me to you.

" That has been the letter-box into which was destined to be dropped the last chapter of this story.

" Like a certain patch of ground in a certain cemetery somewhere is destined to receive your body—one day—and also Sandra's. Or a certain part of England or of the world is destined to see your ashes and Sandra's ashes scattered over it.

" All seems to be pre-destined, brother. Mother and father met—years ago—as part of **their** pre-destined plan for living.

" Somewhere—a corner in a road was fashioned by a gang of workmen—and that corner was to be the corner round which mother and father were to meet their deaths—together.

" I was destined to be born—indeterminate.

" The doctors, the specialists, the perverts and the inverts, the thousands of people, big and small, who have had a hand in my sex transformation, were destined to play their parts.

" And Antonio was to be the man I would really love—when it was too late to go on loving.

" If I do not do this thing—I will live a little longer only. And in great torment—for the pain is almost unbearable. Then the time would come when I would be **forced** into hospital—there to be kept alive for as long as possible in order to satisfy the ethics of the medical profession, to have God's Will done according to the church—and to satisfy the red-taped State.

" So—I prefer **this** way out.

" It is far more graceful.

" The world will know why I have taken my life—but I will not have become a disgusting object tolerated by nurses and protected from the revolted world by the mercy of hospitalisation.

" Take care of yourself—brother. Make good in your practice.

" Warn others who may consult you of the dreadful penalties one has to pay for doing what I have done.

" Do not, at any time, blame yourself for my death. Had you not helped me and encouraged me to have the operation—by now —I would have lost my reason or would have been in and out of prison as a persistent pervert.

" I will not give you Sandra's address. She is not good for you.

" If you see her again—show her this letter. She will see in the papers—soon enough—what has happened to me. I am glad I was able to see her, once again.

" I cannot face seeing **you** again—and for that you must forgive me. I know you would plead for me to go into hospital. Would spend all you have in the world in an attempt to have me cured.

" But there is **no** cure.

" That is final and irrevocable. And I do not think I would very much want to go on living—in any case—were there nothing wrong with me.

" Life was growing very wearisome. It was not all fun—being a man-woman, after all.

" So—goodbye, brother. If they find me in the lake—I suppose you will have me buried somewhere respectable. But not—please—with, or anywhere near, mother and father. They, after all, started it all by dreaming me up one night in a fit of careless passion.

" And I don't think I have ever really forgiven them for that ".

" As soon as I had read this letter ", wrote Juliet's brother, " I travelled immediately to the Lake District. I arrived the very next morning, in the half light of a furious dawn.

" And—as part of what Juliet would have called the pre-destined scheme—I found my way, by getting in touch with the local police—to the lakeside at the very moment searchers, in the light of flares, and with the angry waters of the lake lashing on to the shore—were pulling the naked body of Juliet out of the water.

" She had chosen to take off all her clothes that bitter, early morning, and to walk calmly forward to her death.

" And that is the end of the story of Julian and Juliet.

" Two amazing people with one mind and one body. Two complete personalities at eternal war the one with the other.

" There was one decision, however, that was common to both.

" And that was the brave way out ".

11

PERSONAL ANALYSIS AND QUESTIONNAIRE

There will have been four classes of individual who will have read this book and they will have been both male and female.

There will have been the doctor, the psychologist, the sensation-seeker and, lastly, the man who knows he, himself, suffers from the desire to cross-dress. This man is the transvestite.

If his mental and physical condition is very deep-rooted, he may be a trans-sexual personality—the man who ardently and earnestly desires the body of a woman and to be rid of all masculine characteristics. Of the two—the trans-sexualist is the more serious case. For him there is the wish to become wholly a woman.

The transvestite is usually content to dress in private as a female—or among knowing and understanding friends, or is happy to wear feminine clothing in secret.

In England—provided a panel of doctors and magistrates have decided, beyond doubt, that a man's sanity will be seriously strained if he is forced to go on living as a man—the full trans-sexual operation may be performed upon him. This can be done —in some circumstances, under the National Health Scheme. Otherwise—by private treatment.

The law of England also allows a man to have his Birth certificate altered to that of a female for all lawful and official purposes if his case is proved to be desperate, or if suicide or mental derangement could result through his aberration.

But—a man who dresses in female garb in public places is liable to arrest for creating a public nuisance or through causing a breach of the peace or for suspected soliciting for immoral purposes.

The man who contents himself to dress, in the privacy of his own home, in feminine clothes, does not offend against the law. If he chooses to wear female underwear secretly, by day, under-
234

neath his normal clothes, unbeknown and unsuspected by those with whom he associates, he offends no one.

If he behaves this way with his wife, and **she accepts it,** he is not guilty of mental cruelty and does not furnish grounds for divorce.

If he appears on stage as a female impersonator—he commits no offence. This kind of performance—on the Continent—is extremely popular and the transvestis—as they are called—are considered real artistes.

Unbeknown to the public, unsuspected in office, shop and factory, and in family life—there goes the man who—for a life-time—has to hug the secret urge to cross-dress entirely to himself. He cannot share it with anyone. If unmarried—he dare not mention it to his girl friend. If married—his whole family life would collapse around him were he to betray himself.

This is the man who has the heaviest burden to carry. This is the strongest character. The man who can live his life from youth to old age and find satisfaction, by himself, and be disciplined by its confines.

If—on the other hand—the frustration is so great and reaches trans-sexual proportions—he should confide in his doctor. If his doctor is a good man, and a psychiatric consultation is arranged, and if the psychiatrist is trained to understand this particular aberration—the trans-sexual sufferer should be able to decide whether or not he has the courage to have a phalloctomy in order to complete a sex-change.

And if the Board of specialists and magistrates decides in his favour—he should face up to the operation with fortitude. But it is a serious step to take. Much soul-searching is necessary before the final decision is made.

The transvestite—the cross-dresser—who gets pleasure and satisfaction from wearing feminine underwear in secret has solved his problem. If he likes to dress fully as a female in private—or with friends—he again fulfils himself.

If he is a homosexual (which, let it be stressed, as it has been, in this book) he is a **different personality-type** from the transvestite or trans-sexual. He must either try to overcome his homosexual urges or practises them in private with consenting individuals **who are not youths**. He must **not**—under any consideration whatsoever

—give offence to the public or to any person at all who is devoid of homosexual leanings.

Homosexuality becomes an offence when it offends the public, contaminates and/or perverts boys and youths or is demonstrated in any way whatsoever to members of the female sex. It is an offence to be photographed in homosexual circumstances—even for private viewing by friends in the know.

It is an offence to be photographed in homosexual circumstances, knowing that these photographs are to be sold under the counter in shops.

It is an offence to show photographs of homosexual acts because this constitutes **publication** of obscene, pornographic photographs.

It is an offence to take, sell, publish or even to **show** such works. And this applies equally to photographs demonstrating obscene scenes posed by members of opposite sexes.

Such laws are enforced to prevent the corruption of boys and youths and young girls. These laws assist family life to be unsmirched and untouched by the seamy side of sexuality. The laws governing the soliciting of men by men seek to prevent corruption of the innocent and encouragement of the guilty..

But Man—under the hypnotic and all-powerful sway of sexual aberration, becomes weak-willed but strong in the flesh. He sometimes knows no limits of decency in his search for an outlet. In the heat of the sexual moment he will go berserk. Penalties for such behaviour are severe and rightly so. Sex in the hands of the sexually uncontrolled is a dangerous and potent power for evil.

The man who suffers from homosexual or transvestite tendencies and who controls them and keeps them on a proper level is to be admired more than condemned. Most sexual aberrations are of the mind and the mind **can be controlled and disciplined**.

The transvestite personality sometimes wishes to be with girls —himself dressed as a girl—and to be accepted by them **as** a girl. There would be no sexual demonstrations. He would walk and talk with them, discuss womanly subjects, posture and gesture as they do. He identifies himself with them and they accept him as one of them.

On the other hand—the transvestite may wish to be amongst men—himself dressed as a girl—and to be accepted by the men **as** a girl. Again—no sexual activity would take place.

This is, in itself, harmless enough. The situation exists only in the **mind of the man**. Within the secret recesses of his mind he plays the part of a girl for the duration of the ' scene '. When it is over—he is satisfied and happy. And, until the urge to repeat the act arises again—he is content to continue life as a man, working at a masculine job, loving his wife and children. When the urge overcomes him again, he has to satisfy it once more.

Less fortunate individuals have to wait until their home is empty and then seize the opportunity to dress in female clothes and view themselves in a mirror—imagining what girls (or men) would see if they were present.

Gifted transvestites can become stage artistes and female impersonators. But—by and large—the game of pretending to be a woman is a lonely pursuit. Its satisfaction in privacy is its safest outlet.

Here are two sets of questions — one for the man who suspects himself of being a transvestite — and one for the man who thinks he has trans-sexual tendencies. Advice as to what to do if one is a trans-sexualist has been given in this chapter — i.e., consultations with a doctor and a psychiatrist and a choice as to whether to have an operation or not. Advice for what to do if one is a cross-dresser (transvestite) has just been read — and PRIVACY OF PRACTICE *suggested as the best way of overcoming frustration. Unless — of course — one has sympathetic friends who understand — or who are of a like mind.*

TRANSVESTITE TENDENCIES   YES   NO

Do you recall looking over your mother's or sister's clothes with interest—when a young boy ?

Do you recall envying mother/sister or girls in general, their grace of movement, their hair, the clothes they wore ?

Do you remember ever trying on your mother's/ sister's clothes—or the clothes of any girl when you were between the ages of seven and sixteen ?

Do you think/know your parents wished for a girl instead of a boy and was this ever made plain to you in so many words ?

TRANSVESTITE TENDENCIES　　　　　　　YES　NO

Do you recall being fascinated in any way by the ease with which girls could show off what they were wearing and being envious of this ?

Were you ever involved in any dressing-up games with mother, sister or girl in your childhood ?

Did your mother insist on keeping you in young boy's clothes long after you should have been wearing long trousers ?

Did she make you wear dresses and girlish underwear long after it was proper for you to do so ?

Did your father ever try to treat you more as a girl than a boy ?

Were you forbidden to play ' rough ' games as a boy, forbidden to climb trees, join ' gangs ', be a real boy ?

Was your mother always playing on your emotions —drawing attention to herself and taking you away from your boy companions ?

Did your parents encourage you to mix more wth little girls than with little boys ?

Was a great fuss made of the way you wore your hair ?

In your teens—did you quickly outgrow the bi-sexual age when you were equally divided between affections for boys and girls ?

Did you have schoolboy ' crushes ' on other school-boys and did they persist well on into your late schooldays ?

Did gushing women friends call you a pretty boy— make a fuss of you and generally mollycoddle you ?

　　　If you have to answer ' YES ' to most of these questions—it is obvious that transvestite tendencies were cultivated in your

TRANSVESTITE TENDENCIES   YES   NO

childhood and adolescence—mainly by your parents. It is possible
to cure yourself of your present transvestite tendencies by remem-
bering these vital incidents in your young days and realising **how
futile and ill-conceived they were.** They existed in the minds and
in the actions of **others**—close to you. Had that not been so—it
is very possible and most likely that—today—you would have no
transvestite tendencies whatsoever. You **can** decide—now—
whether to go on living in the past or facing up to the present,
which is now so very different. What your parents liked in those
far-off days—society may not like **today**.

Realise that—as a transvestite—you **are** living largely in the
past and are forever trying to recapture and to retain the pleasur-
able physical and emotional sensations caused by display, show-
ing-off, adulation, the feel of soft, feminine silks and satins and
nylons. That you are living a subconscious life of remembered
happiness and security. Realise that it is by no means **fun** being a
female. Women suffer far more than men—emotionally and
physically. They are permitted their compensations of dressing-up
and making themselves attractive.

TRANS-SEXUAL TENDENCIES   YES   NO

*(the desire to possess female organs and to be without
male organs)*

Do you recall your mother/nurse or father, in your
childhood, making undue fuss of your genital
regions during bath times or at any other times ?

Were you ever told by your parents or by little girls
that boys' genitals were nasty, ugly, repulsive,
unnecessary ?

Do you remember ' little boy ' scenes with little
girls when you admired the absence of visible
genitals in girls and wished yours were invisible
also ?

Were there incidents in your boyhood and/or
adolescent days when older girls expressed disgust
or disdain at your genitals or made fun of you for
being awkward and ungainly and unattractive ?

TRANS-SEXUAL TENDENCIES   YES   NO

Do you remember hating your genitals and wishing you could cut them off or hide them in some way ?

Can you remember being overpoweringly attracted by girls' clothes—especially by their underwear ?

Did you form the habit of pausing outside lingerie shops and looking in the windows ?

Was there a time when you secretly bought yourself some feminine underwear and wore it in front of a mirror—in front of a girl—in front of a boy or in front of your sister or mother ?

If so—were you reprimanded or chastised—or were you admired and encouraged by mother, sister, girl or boy ?

Do you remember looking in mirrors and taking a great interest in your body ? Wishing you had breasts ? Putting on a bra to see how it looked ?

Did you develop, at about adolescence—an admiration for your body and did you begin to try to develop a small waist, or attempt to promote breasts, or to shave off bodily hair ?

Did you experiment with make-up in front of a mirror to try to make yourself look pretty ?

Can you recall consciously and purposely walking like a girl, moving your hands and fingers in effeminate ways, sitting down, cross-legged like a girl ?

Did you regret it when your voice broke and you lost the falsetto note ?

Did you ever try, when young, to expose yourself to girls—dressed as a girl, in girls' clothes or in girls' underwear ?

TRANS-SEXUAL TENDENCIES   YES NO

In your first love-making experiments with girls—
were you apt to want to be passive and to be made
love to rather than make love yourself ?

Did it please you if girls were more maternally
inclined towards you than loving ?

Was your mother the image you held in your mind
of the perfect female ?
Or your sister ?

Were you, when young, approached by, or enter-
tained by, men with effeminate natures, who petted
you and made you feel weak and resisting and
feminine ?

When very young, were dolls your toys instead of
engines, playing ' mothers and fathers ' one of your
favourite games rather than soldiers ?

Did you find yourself approaching adolescence with
a strong and definite envy and jealousy of girls with
their pretty faces, their privileges over the male ?

Were you, as a youth, more artistic and creative
than constructive and mechanical ?

Did you have an overwhelming interest in domestic
things like cooking, making beds, keeping the home
tidy, embroidery, looking after baby brothers or
sisters or other people's babies ?

Did you make a fool of yourself with your first real
sex adventure with a girl, being incapable of effect-
iveness through shame or through the ridicule or
the disgust shown by the girl ?

Was your first sex experience of a homosexual
nature—with a youth or with a man ?

If you have to answer ' YES ' to most of these questions, the
female side of your nature certainly predominates. This may have
been inherent in you at birth as has been explained in the story

you have just read of Julian and Juliet. On the other hand—
parents, teachers, friends, girls—may have injected into your mind
the desirability of femininity as opposed to masculinity. You may
have developed a ' castration-complex '—a desire to be rid of your
male member. This may have been self-induced or brought about
by those with whom you came into contact in your early, formative
years.

Realise that—as a trans-sexual personality— **you** also are
living a great deal in the past. But, apart from the desire to dress
as a female you actually want to deny manhood and **live** as a
female. While the operation for removal of the male organs has its
compensations—it is certainly a desperate solution to your problem. And a dangerous one.

While the personality in this book developed cancer as a
result of the operation and sexual activity after the operation—it
is by no means true that cancer **would** or **could** develop as an
after-effect. Indeed—leading trans-sexual personalities in the last
few decades have proved to be highly successful cases, have been
delightful people, taking their place in society and in the world of
entertainment and their health and intellect has been well above
average.

These people—and more, besides—who have never had any
press publicity—were shining examples of perfect subjects for the
sex-transformation.

One can never be sure, however. Any more than one can be
sure **anyone** will recover from **any** sort of operation, or that bad
after-effects will not set in—in due course. Therefore—the strictest
caution is naturally advised—whatever tumult of mind might have
to be endured.

It is possible for a man to lead a perfectly normal, happy life,
to be married and have children, a good job and a good home—
and yet to be able to live with the cross of transvestite or even
trans-sexual desires on his shoulders—provided he is determined
to keep this thing in its right perspective and not to let it become
an **obsession**.

Many men love embroidery, housework, cooking and other
feminine pursuits. In these diversions they work-off the female
sides of their natures in the same way in which women who become
car mechanics, handymen around the house, career-women and so
on—work off the masculine sides of **their** natures.

Women are, altogether, far more adaptable to these sexual kinks and quirks than are men. This may be because society is more tolerant of the ' kinky ' woman. Or perhaps does not recognise feminine ' kinkiness '—in any case. And—even though women are prone to hysterical states of mind as a direct result of possessing a womb and all the trivia of motherhood—they are—in the long run—far more at grips with sexual problems than are men.

Society is certainly less tolerant of the ' kinky ' man.

This is because man is a responsible member of society insomuch as he is the creator of life in the very first place and his function of fatherhood should not be abused or mis-directed.

He may run a beauty-parlour, be a hairdresser, design fashion for the women of the world, write, compose, paint and sculpt, but —apart from contributing to the arts and to industry—he is also expected to contribute to the propogation of children in order to keep the human race going. This function, therefore—he should put first and foremost, allowing his deviations to take a second place.

Most certainly—man should not be encouraged to pervert others—either of his own or his opposite sex. In the throes of sexual doubt, however, he must be tolerated, helped and assisted either to overcome his aberration or be allowed to express it, harmlessly, with no detriment to others—and not to be ridiculed, hounded or ' witch-hunted ' in the process.

The most tragic thing that can happen to a boy-child is to be born with an overdose of feminine characteristics that, later in life, force themselves to the surface. And the most damnable thing parents can do to their male children is to cultivate, encourage or nurture feminine desires or tendencies that, buried deep in the subconscious—resurrect themselves later in life and make the male child's life a private hell on earth.

*GLOSSARY of terms extracted from . . .

"THE NEW DICTIONARY OF PSYCHOLOGY"
by Philip Lawrence Harriman, and published by . . .
THE PHILOSOPHICAL LIBRARY INC., NEW YORK, and having a special bearing on the subject-matter of this book.

adrenal glands : endocrine glands adjacent to the kidneys. The adrenal medulla secretes adrenalin (epinephrin) in states of intense emotion; the adrenal cortex supplies a hormone known as cortin. Hyperfunctioning of the adrenal cortex in childhood causes precocious puberty in males, and a condition of masculinity in females. In adult women, hyperfunctioning of the cortex results in a condition known as virilism, in which excess hair appears on the face and sex functions are inhibited.

association-test : the method devised by Jung (1910) in which the subject responds to each of one hundred discreet words, thereby revealing abnormal associations.

auto-eroticism : achievement of sexual pleasure by manipulation of one's own erogenous zones.

castration complex : psychoanalyst's term to describe the fear of genitals because of forbidden erotic desires.

clitoris : the female counterpart of the male's penis, an erectile organ situated on the ischiopubic rami.

---

*NOTE : This Glossary has been abbreviated to explain certain sections of this book—and these brief extracts by no means represent the full text of " The New Dictionary of Psychology " which is, in fact, an extremely informative volume, fully recommended to the student.

erectile tissues : multicellular groups containing expansile capillaries which, when stimulated, become erect (e.g., penis, breasts, clitoris), and hence are included in the erogenous zones (Freud).

erotomania : obsessive interests in sex; nymphomania or satyriasis.

eunuchoid build : a bodily build resembling that of the eunuch (castrated male), and resulting from underdevelopment of gonads. A variety of types has been described, some writers emphasising the infantile or childish appearance, the feminine type of hips, scanty hair in pubic area, and hypogenitalism.

exhibitionism : in the narrow sense, exposure of genitals. According to psychoanalysis, the exposure is usually done in the presence of a person who represents the Oedipus situation. In a broad sense, the term is used to connote various attention-getting activities.

fetishism : erotic attachment to an object which symbolises the person to whom it belongs. Hair, shoes, handkerchief, and the like, may have fetishistic value.

frigidity : absence of sex desires in a woman. According to psychoanalysts, it may be attributed to the castration complex, repressed incestuous feelings, or homosexual tendencies.

homoerotic: attraction to members of the same sex for outlets for erotic desires.

homogenitalism : libidinous desires for members of the same sex.

homosexuality : a term used in psychoanalysis to denote the second stage in personality development, which is that of attraction to members of the same sex (the first being auto-eroticism; the final being heteroeroticism).

heterosexuality : normal sex adjustment.

hermaphroditism : bisexualism; having both ovaries and testes.

heteroeroticism : attraction to members of the opposite sex.

hyperaphrodisia : the condition of satyriasis or nymphomania.

iconolagny : form of sex perversion in which gratification is achieved by looking at lewd pictures or in interpreting works of art in a pornographic manner.

infantile sexuality : the psychoanalytic doctrine that the unconscious wishes of the adult are closely related to sex wishes of the first five years of life. Thus, the psychoneurotic adult or the immature adult unconsciously seeks gratification of infantile sex drives through wit, dreams, phantasies, and other mechanisms.

impotence : inability to achieve an orgasm. It may arise from organic or psychic factors.

inversion : the assumption of the role of a member of the opposite sex.

Lesbian : female homosexual. The term comes from the name of the island of Lesbia, where Sappho lived.

machlaenomania : masochism (in a female); sexual perversion in which pleasure is afforded by pain.

machlosyne : nymphomaniac, a woman with inordinate sex desires.

masochism : erotic gratification in being beaten. The term was taken (by Freud) from part of the name of Luther von Sacher-Masoch (1835-1895), an Austrian novelist who used this theme in his stories. Masochism may be actual (implying the use of whips or other means of inflicting physical pain) or symbolic (finding reasons to revel in self-pity).

narcissism : abnormal self-love; hence, according to Freudians, the inversion of the libido. Primary narcissism is the original, infantile direction of the libido upon the body before the object-love stage. A person with a defective capacity for object-love is said, by analysts, to be a narcissist.

nymphomania : uncontrollable and insatiable sex desires in a woman. A similar condition in a man is known as ' satyriasis '.

onanism : coitus interruptus. Often (though incorrectly), masturbation.

orgasm : the height of genital excitation.

ovum : the female germ-cell.

penis-envy : according to psychoanalysis, a stage through which many little girls go when they discover that they are unlike males, and hence they believe themselves handicapped and ill-treated.

priapism : a persistent erection of the penis due to a nervous lesion, not to erotic desires.

pederastery : intercourse ' per anum '.

psychosomatic : pertaining to both mind and body.

sadism : a form of sex perversion in which cruelty, ill-treatment, and suffering are inflicted upon the love-object. The earliest form is said to be oral sadism (biting) and both anal and urethral sadism may develop during toilet training. The term has been extended to include any type of pleasure achieved through the infliction of pain upon another. Freud coined the word from the name of the Marquis de Sade (1740-1814), a French novelist.

satyriasis : excessive sex desire in a male.

sapphism : Lesbianism, or female homosexuality.

self-abuse : a popular term for masturbation, which was once believed to be the cause for serious mental disorders.

sex character : any trait, mental or physical, which differentiates the sexes. Primary sex characters are those which are directly involved in reproduction; secondary sex characters are those which have no direct bearing upon reproductive functions but which differentiate the sexes.

sex differences : those which are found in psychological tests and measures to differentiate the sexes, the traditional debate being whether or not measured deviations in mental tests indicate the existence of inherent differences.

sterilisation : an operation (on human beings) which involves cutting the vas deferens (in males) and cutting or excising the fallopian tubes (in females), and which has been advocated by eugenicists as a means of combatting the " rising tide of the biologically unfit ".

transvestism : the adoption of clothing and mannerisms of the opposite sex.

testes : two glands in the scrotum which secrete spermatozoa.

tribadism : production of the orgasm by friction without the insertion of the penis into the vagina. Also, friction between two females.

uranism : homosexuality. Karl Heinrichs coined the term in 1862, denoting the male homosexual ' uraning ' and the female ' urinde '.

urethral eroticism : sexual pleasure by the male in urination. According to psychoanalysts, the male can experience greater pleasure from the act because the urethra is about 8 to 9 inches long in the male; in the female, it is only about 1½ inches long.

vagina : canal from vulvar opening to cervix of uterus in the female.

voyeur : one who achieves erotic gratification by watching a member of the opposite sex undress. In symbolic voyeurism, erotic impulses are stimulated by reading pornographic litera-ture, viewing lewd pictures, and the like. Voyeurs find gratification in watching coitus.

vulva : external parts of female genitalia.

zone, erogenous : area of the body which, when stimulated, affords sexual pleasure.